POROMERICS

IN THE

SHOE INDUSTRY

POROMERICS
in the shoe industry

Edited by

Dr. A. R. PAYNE

Director, SATRA

ELSEVIER PUBLISHING COMPANY LIMITED

AMSTERDAM – LONDON – NEW YORK

1970

ELSEVIER PUBLISHING COMPANY LIMITED
BARKING, ESSEX, ENGLAND

ELSEVIER PUBLISHING COMPANY
335 JAN VAN GALENSTRAAT P.O. BOX 211, AMSTERDAM
THE NETHERLANDS

AMERICAN ELSEVIER PUBLISHING COMPANY INC.
52 VANDERBILT AVENUE, NEW YORK, N.Y. 10017

0 444 20066 5

LIBRARY OF CONGRESS CATALOGUE CARD NUMBER 71–122959

With 162 Illustrations and 50 Tables

COMPOSED AND PRINTED BY PERIDON LTD, LONDON, NW9

Preface

DR A. R. PAYNE
Director, SATRA

IT WOULD be of advantage as an introduction to this book of the proceedings of the Poromerics Symposium, if we defined what a 'poromeric' is.

A poromeric may be defined as a man-made shoe upper material which is generally similar in nature and appearance to leather and, in particular, has comparable permeability to water vapour.

This is quite a wide definition and some may disagree with it; but I think we must now start to define these types of materials and give them some form of generic name, and poromeric is the only one so far conjured up to cover the materials discussed in this work.

Poromeric materials which are currently available on the market are: Ortix*, Skailen, Hi-Telac, Clarino, Patora, Aztran, Corfam, Belesa and also a Porous Plastics poromeric—Porvair.

This list covers the materials that are to be discussed, and are in the most part available to shoe manufacturers.

Now, of course, this is the tip of an iceberg, and, in fact, we are at the stage when we are going to be subjected to quite a lot more poromeric materials and there will be the real problem of evaluating them to face.

Not only do we have the poromeric uppers as such but permeable shoe linings come into this category: such materials as Porolux, Corane, Mombassa and Ceef, are now being offered to the shoe industry.

The Poromerics Symposium presented many aspects of the impact of poromerics on the shoe manufacturing industry. I believe it is fair to claim that the proceedings of this symposium represent the first comprehensive collection of scientific and technological information in this important new branch of shoe technology.

*No longer available.

The Poromerics Symposium

was held by the Shoe and Allied Trade Research Association

at the Assembly Halls, Civic Centre, Corby, Northants,

on September 24 and 25, 1968

Contents

LIST OF PLATES

CHAPTER 1

Mechanical effects between layers in poromerics

C. E. WEBB

SUMMARY

A NUMBER of poromerics have been compared by studying the physical characteristics of strains which occur normally in the upper during lasting. The degree of correlation between these physical characteristics and lasting behaviour, as assessed qualitatively, has been studied. The ratio of modulus at directions of 90° to one another, elastic recovery at 10% extension, and resilience at 10% extension has been related to lasting performance. A poromeric containing no fabric layer was included in order to compare its behaviour with the more conventional poromerics containing fabric. Comparisons of the stress-strain characteristics of the individual components have also been studied.

TYPES OF POROMERIC

Four types of poromerics were compared, and Fig. 1.1 illustrates the difference in construction. It will be seen that poromerics A and B are very similar, the main difference being in the weave and fibre size of the fabric reinforcing material.

Poromeric C contains no fabric layer and poromeric D is, in a sense, intermediate between A and C in that it contains a fabric layer which is in the bonded fibre layer rather than between the microporous layer and the bonded fibre layer. A sample of Kip leather was used as a reference material.

MEASUREMENT OF LASTING STRAINS

In order to ascertain the strains occurring during machine lasting, lattice lines were printed at intervals of 5 mm in lengthwise and widthwise directions on the poromerics before cutting.

The length of the lines was measured before and after lasting and the increase or decrease calculated as a percentage of the unstrained length.

A schematic presentation of the lattice lines in relation to their position on the toe, vamp, and heel is shown in Fig. 1.2. The forepart strains for three poromerics are shown in Table 1.1, and those in the heel in Table 1.2. They demonstrate that in the toe area the most severe

strain may lead to extensions of up to 23% in the case of the lower
modulus materials and up to 13% for the material of higher modulus.

PHYSICAL CHARACTERISTICS OF THE POROMERICS

In order to visualize the effect of such strains on the poromeric material
the stress-strain curves for two directions at extensions up to 20% are
shown in Figs. 1.3 and 1.4. These curves were determined using an
Instron type tensile tester and a test specimen of thickness shown in
Table 1.3 which gives in detail the physical measurements made.
Samples were cut to a strip 2 cm wide and 20 cm long. The distance
between the clamps was 10 cm and the speed of separation 10 cm/min.
Definitions of some of the properties measured are shown in Fig. 1.5.

It will be seen that there are some marked differences in the behaviour
of the four poromerics as denoted by their curves. A and B most
resemble the sample of Kip leather used as a reference material. D is
unique in its similar stress-strain characteristics in both directions
and its high modulus. C is a low modulus material.

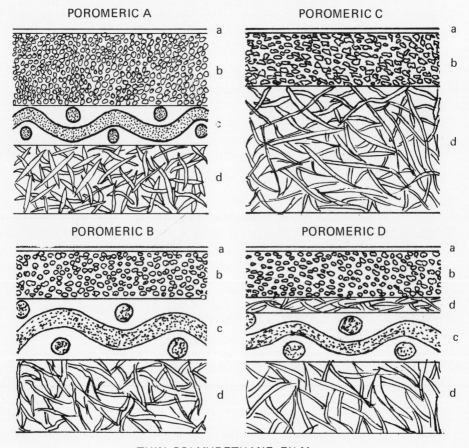

a—THIN POLYURETHANE FILM
b—MICROPOROUS POLYURETHANE FILM
c—FABRIC
d—BONDED FIBRE

Fig. 1.1.

2

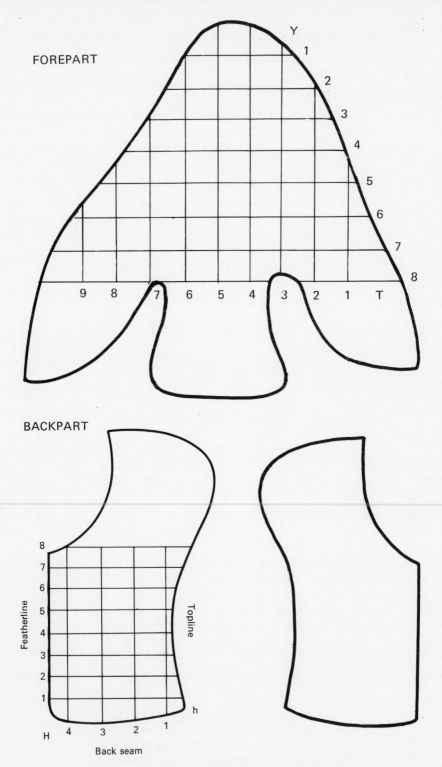

Fig. 1.2. A schematic presentation of the lattice lines on uppers for measurement of lasting strains.

Table 1.1. Dimensional changes of forepart of poromeric shoe uppers on toe lasting (%)

Poromeric Lattice line No.	B	C	D
Y – 1	10	23	10
Y – 2	13	18	9
Y – 3	10	16	9
Y – 4	7	10	6
Y – 5	6	13	8
Y – 6	2	9	5
Y – 7	2	4	4
Y – 8	3	5	3
Average	7	13	7
T – 1	–3	–	1
T – 2	–2	4	2
T – 3	–2	4	4
T – 4	4	3	3
T – 5	1	2	2
T – 6	0	3	2
T – 7	–1	–4	2
T – 8	1	–3	3
T – 9	–3	4	5
Average	0	2	3

MODULUS MEASUREMENTS

One of the most obvious characteristics of most poromerics and leather is the different stress-strain effects when measured in directions at right angles. This has been termed stretch anisotropy and has been described by L. G. Hole and J. G. Butlin [1]

This property is mainly influenced by the presence of a fabric layer but will also be affected by the bonded fibre layer and to a lesser extent by the microporous 'grain layer'. A method of assessing this difference in stretch with direction is to measure the ratio of the modulus along the length and width of the material (as determined by the warp and weft of the fabric layer or the fibre grain in the bonded fibre layer). The ratio of modulus length/modulus width might be expected to vary with elongation. When all the fabric interlayer fibres are fully stretched, they will have similar stress-strain characteristics in both directions. The modulus ratio at higher elongations will then be characteristic of the bonded fibre layer, the microporous layer, and the polymer used in the fibres and not of the weave of the fabric.

On this supposition a poromeric containing no layer of fabric would be expected to show little difference in the ratio of the modulus length/modulus width over a range of elongations, whereas that containing fabric would be expected to show a variation. The results of plotting the ratio of modulus length/modulus width are shown in Fig. 1.6. In this case the poromeric containing no fabric behaved more or less as predicted giving an almost constant ratio of modulus length/modulus width. Since leather is a type of bonded fibre with no fabric interlayer this behaved similarly. At elongations of above 15% poromerics A and B have modulus ratios similar to leather. This could be taken to indicate that the anisotropic effect of the fabric layer is almost eliminated at elongations of greater than 15%. D shows the same type of curve as A and B, although the ratios are much lower for all elongations. This arises from the low modulus of such materials due to the nature and location of the fabric layer in the bonded fibre layer.

ELASTIC RECOVERY

Another significant property of the poromeric which may determine the lasting properties of the material is the elastic recovery as defined in Fig. 1.5. It is evident from previous results that at 10% extension there is no breakdown of the fabric layer. Therefore, the elastic recovery will be related mainly to the effect of the bonded fibre layer and the microporous layer since most fabrics will not be stretched enough to extend their individual fibres but only the crimp of the

Table 1.2. Dimensional changes of back part of poromeric shoe uppers on back seat lasting (%)

Poromeric / Lattice line No.	B	C	D
H – 1	2	5	2
H – 2	2	3	2
H – 3	2	2	2
H – 4	2	3	8
H – 5	2	3	8
H – 6	2	3	8
H – 7	2	2	5
H – 8	2	2	3
Average	2	3	5
h – 1	1	4	3
h – 2	3	4	5
h – 3	2	3	2
h – 4	2	2	1
Average	2	3	3

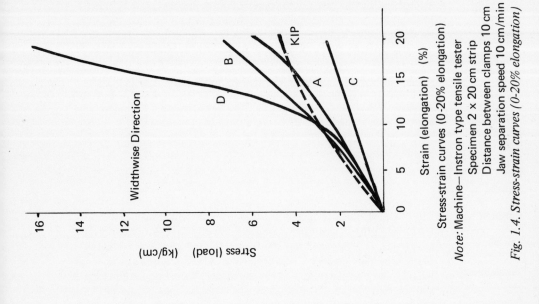

Widthwise Direction

Stress-strain curves (0-20% elongation)

Note: Machine—Instron type tensile tester
Specimen 2 x 20 cm strip
Distance between clamps 10 cm
Jaw separation speed 10 cm/min

Fig. 1.4. Stress-strain curves (0-20% elongation)

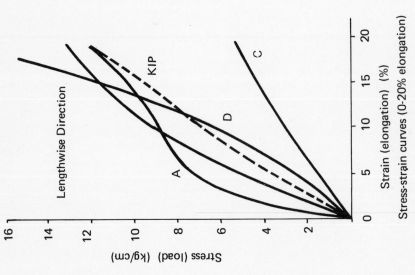

Lengthwise Direction

Stress-strain curves (0-20% elongation)

Note: Machine—Instron type tensile tester
Specimen 2 x 20 cm strip
Distance between clamps 10 cm
Jaw separation speed 10 cm/min

Fig. 1.3. Stress-strain curves (0-20% elongation).

material. The elastic recovery curves for the four poromerics are shown in Figs. 1.7 and 1.8. In the lengthwise direction A, B, and leather form one group, and C and D another. In the widthwise direction there is much less difference between the poromerics. It might be expected that for these types of material the higher the modulus at a given extension the lower would be the elastic recovery at the same extension, since more work has been expended in extending the material and disturbing its structure.

If the modulus at 10% is plotted against the recovery at 10% extension, a number of points are obtained which suggest that there is an approximately straight line relationship between the two properties (Fig. 1.9).

Table 1.3. Tensile properties and elasticity of shoe upper materials

Material		Poromeric A		Poromeric B		Poromeric C		Poromeric D		Leather (Kip)	
Direction		*L*	*W*	*L*	*W*	*L*	*W*	*L*	*W*	*L*	*W*
Thickness	mm	1·49		1·55		1·46		1·69		1·22	
Tensile strength	kg/cm kg/cm^2	14·4 97	10·8 72	14·3 93	10·6 68	9·0 62	6·7 46	15·3 91	18·5 109	42·1 345	27·2 222
Elongation	%	26·0	48·7	23·3	34·3	49·8	100·6	18·8	20·5	58·7	81·3
5% modulus	kg/cm kg/cm^2	6·9 46	1·2 8	4·6 30	1·2 8	1·5 10	0·7 5	2·0 12	1·0 6	3·5 29	1·5 12
10% modulus	kg/cm kg/cm^2	8·7 58	2·3 16	8·6 55	3·0 19·0	3·0 20	1·4 9·5	5·9 35	3·8 22	6·5 53	3·0 25
Elastic recovery at 10% extension	%	70	85	73	82	82	89	80	85	71	72
Resilience at 10% extension	%	30	60	38	6Q	61	67	47	56	43	43

Note: *L* is lengthwise direction and *W* is widthwise direction.

RESILIENCE

When a rubber-like material is stressed and then allowed to return to a position of no stress, the energy expended in extending, is not wholly returned on removing the stress. The difference between the energy input and the energy returned is a measure of the hysteresis. This property can be expressed as resilience and is defined in Fig. 1.5. The importance of this in the tyre industry is well known and in general resilience decreases with modulus. The resilience curves for the four poromerics are shown in Figs. 1.7 and 1.8. The relationship of resilience to modulus up to 10% elongation was also examined and is shown in Fig. 1.10. Other poromerics and leathers not tabulated in Table 1.3 were included to obtain an under-spread of results. It is noted that there is a general relationship between modulus and resilience.

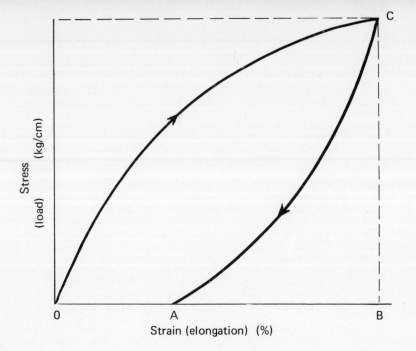

(1) Modulus: CB at OB

(2) Elastic recovery: $\dfrac{AB}{OB} \times 100$

(3) Resilience: $\dfrac{ACB \times 100}{OCB}$

Definition of modulus, elastic recovery and resilience

Fig. 1.5.

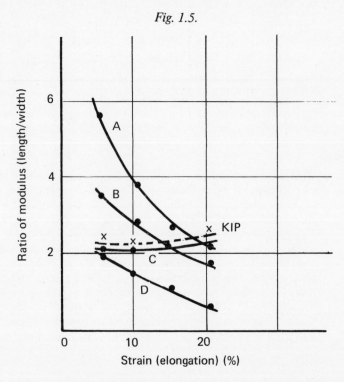

Fig. 1.6. Directional Modulus Ratios at varying elongations.

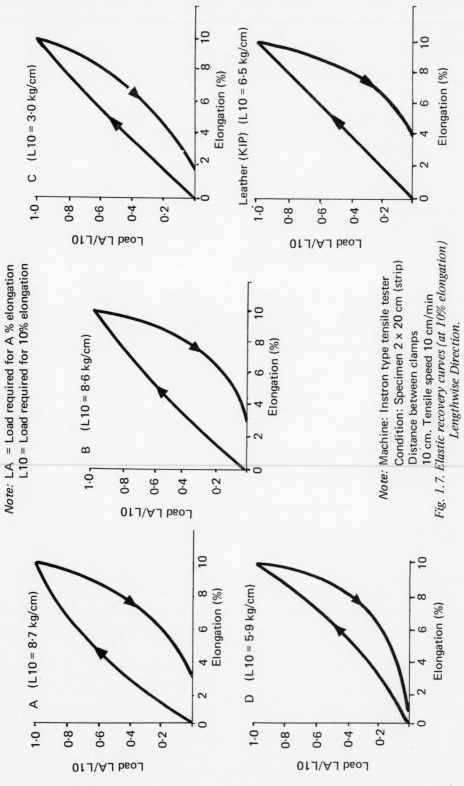

Note: LA = Load required for A % elongation
L10 = Load required for 10% elongation

A (L10 = 8·7 kg/cm)

B (L10 = 8·6 kg/cm)

C (L10 = 3·0 kg/cm)

D (L10 = 5·9 kg/cm)

Leather (KIP) (L10 = 6·5 kg/cm)

Note: Machine: Instron type tensile tester
Condition: Specimen 2 x 20 cm (strip)
Distance between clamps
10 cm. Tensile speed 10 cm/min

Fig. 1.7. Elastic recovery curves (at 10% elongation)
Lengthwise Direction.

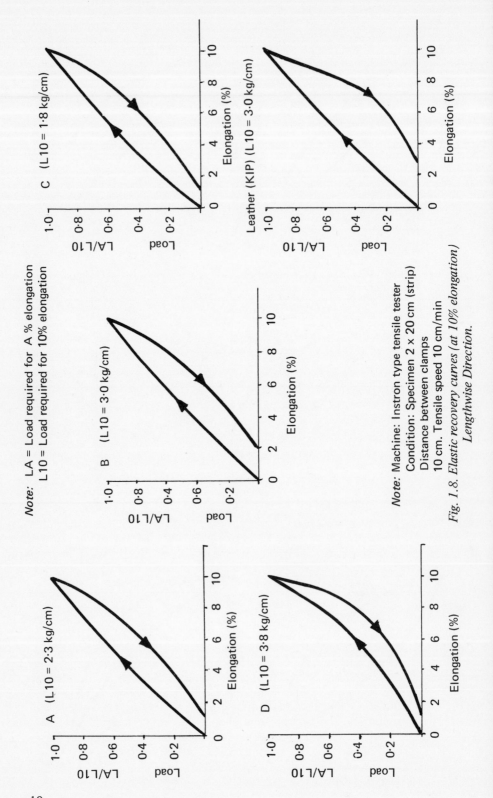

Note: LA = Load required for A % elongation
L10 = Load required for 10% elongation

Note: Machine: Instron type tensile tester
Condition: Specimen 2 x 20 cm (strip)
Distance between clamps
10 cm. Tensile speed 10 cm/min

Fig. 1.8. Elastic recovery curves (at 10% elongation)
Lengthwise Direction.

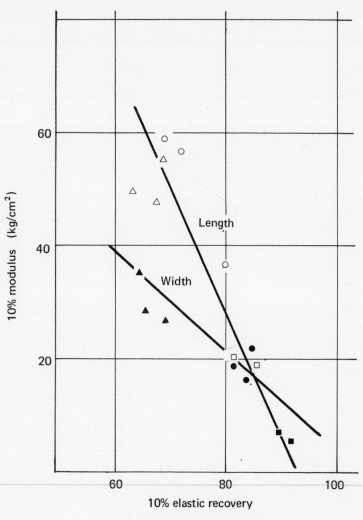

O = Fabric containing poromerics
□ = Non-fabric containing poromerics
△ = Leather

White symbols = Lengthwise determinations
Black symbols = Widthwise determinations

Fig. 1.9.

It might be expected that resilience would be related to the flex life of the material since, in general, materials of high resilience give longer flex life than those of lower resilience. However, at the relatively low frequency of flexing which occurs in service life of footwear, the effect of heat build-up, resulting from low resilience, is unlikely to be noticeable. This has been confirmed by flex tests, which indicate that poromeric D shows the least resistance to cracking as measured on the SATRA vamp flexer, whilst A, B and C are of the same order. The results of these tests are given in Table 1.4.

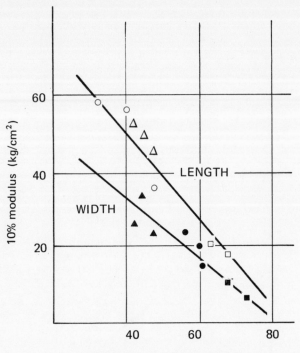

Resilience at 10% extension

○ = Fabric containing poromerics
□ = Non-fabric containing poromerics
△ = Leather

White symbols = Lengthwise determinations
Black symbols = Widthwise determinations

Fig. 1.10.

Table 1.4. Flex fatigue resistance, SATRA vamp flexer (1 000 times)

Poromeric	A	B	C	D
First sign of cracking	Greater than 1 000	Greater than 1 000	Greater than 1 000	200

ANALYSIS OF THE PHYSICAL PROPERTIES OF THE LAYERS OF POROMERICS

To examine the characteristics of each layer and its contribution to the final properties of the complete poromeric, the various poromerics were carefully separated into their various layers by mechanical methods only. This was fairly easy with poromerics A and B, but the microcellular layer could not be removed in one piece in the case of poromeric C. With D, it was not possible to remove the fabric from the bonded fibre layer although the microcellular layer could be separated.

Each layer was then subjected to a 10% extension on the Hounsfield Tensometer. This was followed by a second, third and fourth extension to the same percentage elongation. The results of the first two extensions are shown in Fig. 1.11.

The main characteristics which go to produce the physical properties can be readily seen from these curves. The high modulus of the fabric is obviously the main factor in determining final modulus. It is interesting to note that with poromeric A the recovery of the complete poromeric seems to be higher than the average for the bonded fibre and the fabric, but in B it is much nearer the average. This could indicate more interaction between layers in the case of A.

In poromeric C, the lower loads for a given extension with the bonded fibre layer compared to the complete poromeric leads to the conclusion that the microporous layer has a larger effect on the final stress-strain properties than in the case of A and B. No conclusions can be made with poromeric D from the results obtained.

If a study of Table 1.5 is made the following interesting points are evident.

With poromeric A, during the first extension, the total of the loads for each layer is within experimental error of the load for the complete poromeric, but on the second extension the load for the poromeric is slightly but significantly higher than the sum of the loads for each layer. This applies for the third and fourth extensions, and, as already mentioned, may indicate that there is a mutual reinforcing effect between the layers in the case of A which is less noticeable in case B. This is probably a function of the magnitude of the fabric bond to each of the layers. In the case of poromeric B, it was noted that the fabric could be separated more easily.

On the second extension for A the drop in fabric load at 10% elongation is slightly greater than for B which could again be an indication that after separation the fibres of the fabric in A are a little more impregnated with the adjacent layers than in the case of B. On the second extension, however, the bonds due to the impregnation between fibres have been broken down.

MEASUREMENT OF PRACTICAL LASTING CHARACTERISTICS

The lasting performance of each poromeric was assessed visually using the following machines:

Toe laster:	Astra 78 (Cement lasted)
Side laster:	Kamborian (Cement lasted)
Heel seat laster:	Moenus 1224 (Tack lasted)

Steam activation was used for toe lasting only, but no temperature data is available.

The assessment was made by a factory operator and a technician on the following points:

Analysis of Poromeric Layers

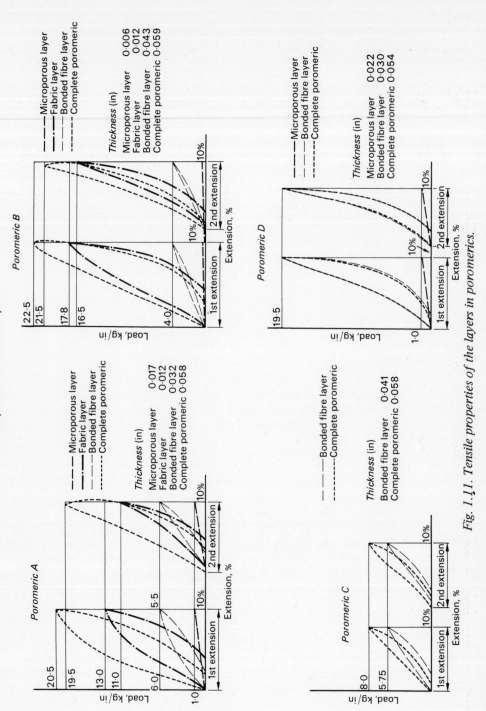

Fig. 1.11. Tensile properties of the layers in poromerics.

14

PLATE 1

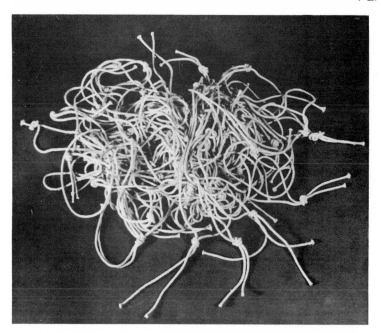

Fig. 2.3. Knotted string model for Mullins effect.

Fig. 2.9. Collagen fibrils: electronmicrograph, 30,000 magnification.

PLATE 2

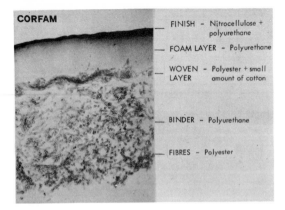

CORFAM

FINISH – Nitrocellulose +
       polyurethane

FOAM LAYER – Polyurethane

WOVEN – Polyester + small
LAYER   amount of cotton

BINDER – Polyurethane

FIBRES – Polyester

Fig. 2.13.

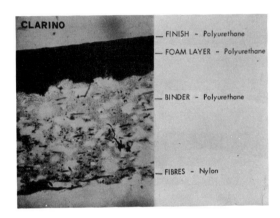

CLARINO

FINISH – Polyurethane

FOAM LAYER – Polyurethane

BINDER – Polyurethane

FIBRES – Nylon

Fig. 2.14.

LEATHER

GRAIN LAYER

CORIUM

FLESH LAYER

Fig. 2.15.

Table 1.5. Analysis of physical properties of poromeric layers

| Poromeric | Type of layer | Load in kg on 1 in wide strip on extending 10% | | | | |
		1st Extension	2nd Extension	3rd Extension	4th Extension	Thickness in
A	Microporous layer	1·0	1·0	1·0	1·0	0·017
	Fabric	13·0	11·0	9·8	9·8	0·012
	Bonded fibre	6·0	5·5	5·5	5·5	0·032
	Total	20·0	17·5	16·3	16·3	0·061
	Complete Poromeric	20·5	19·5	18·75	18·25	0·058
B	Microporous layer	0·2	0·2	0·2	0·2	0·006
	Fabric	17·8	16·5	16·5	16·2	0·012
	Bonded fibre	4·0	3·8	3·8	3·5	0·043
	Total	22·0	20·5	20·5	19·9	0·061
	Complete Poromeric	22·5	21·5	21·0	20·5	0·059
C	Microporous layer	–	–	–	–	
	Bonded fibre	5·75	5·5	5·5	5·25	0·041
	Total	–	–	–	–	
	Complete Poromeric	8·0	7·9	7·8	7·75	0·058
D	Microporous layer	1·0	1·0	1·0	1·0	0·022
	Bonded fibre	19·75	19·5	19·25	19·25	0·030
	Total	20·75	20·5	20·25	20·25	0·052
	Complete Poromeric	19·5	19·25	19·0	19·0	0·054

Strips 1-in, wide and 6-in long were extended to 10% and the extension measured by bench marks set 4-in apart.

1. Friction of the wiper blade on the lasting margins of the uppers
2. Fit to the last
3. Required force to give good lasting
4. Smoothness of the feather line
5. Wrinkles on the lasting margin area

Results are shown in Table 1.6.

Property (1) is likely to be dependent on the friction characteristics of the polyurethane and unrelated to the properties discussed. Properties (2), (3), (4), and (5), however, would be expected to bear a close relationship to the modulus, stretch characteristics, recovery and resilience. The poromerics are shown placed in order of performance in lasting (Table 1.7), in order of decreasing magnitude for the properties already described (Table 1.8) and in order of the shape retention in service in Table 1.9.

From a comparison of these ratings, there appears to be some correlation between lasting performance as measured practically and the physical properties measured. The conclusions drawn from

Table 1.6. Results of lasting performance test on poromeric shoe upper

Poromeric	A	B	C	D
Toe lasting	△	△	○	△
Side lasting	△~○	△~○	○	○
Heel seat lasting	X	△~○	△	○
Total evaluation	X	△	○	△~○

Key: Sign ○ was satisfactory as an upper material
△ was little worse than ○
X unsatisfactory

Table 1.7. Lasting performance of materials

Operation	Toe lasting	Side lasting	Back lasting
Performance (best at top)	C A.B.D.	C.D. A.B.	D C B A

Table 1.8. Ranking of materials according to physical properties

Property	10% modulus L	10% modulus W	Modulus L/W ratio at 10%	Elastic recovery L	Elastic recovery W	Resilience L	Resilience W
Ranking (highest at top)	AB D C	D B A C	A B C D	C D B A	C D.A. B	C D B A	C A.B. D

Table 1.9. Relative shape retention of uppers in service

Property	Shape retention in service
Performance (best at top)	AB C D

the rather limited experimental data would be that the following properties are desirable for satisfactory lasting:

1. Low modulus at 10% extension
2. Low modulus L/W ratio
3. High elastic recovery at 10% extension
4. High resilience at 10% extension

The desirability of a low modulus may be evident for the conditions measured but it should be remembered that it will also give wider variations in lasting margins.

Whilst a low modulus length/modulus width ratio is desirable it is questionable if this should be lower than that obtained with leather to obtain optimum lasting characteristics.

A high elastic recovery and resilience would not be expected to favour lasting but it should be remembered that poromeric C showing more favourable lasting characteristics than A and B has a considerably lower modulus and is extended much more than A and B during lasting. The recovery of C at these higher elongations may be less than that for A and B at the lower elongations.

It is also noted that A and B have higher heat setting characteristics than C and D as shown in Table 1.10, and it is significant that in the toe lasting which was steam activated there is less difference in lasting properties between C and A and B.

Fig. 1.10. Heat setting characteristics

Permanent extension as % of original length

Poromeric / Direction	A	B	C	D
Lengthwise	90	80	73	55
Widthwise	80	80	70	63

Specimens 2 cm wide were marked with 20 cm bench marks and stretched to 10%. They were then subjected to a temperature of 100°C for 30 minutes and the measurement between the bench mark made after 24 hours at room temperature.

CONCLUSION

A and B have shown up rather less favourably than C and D in lasting experiments, although in service, A and B gave the best shape retention, followed by C and D, in that order. No definite conclusions can be made concerning the relationship of the properties measured to lasting since other variables have also to be taken into consideration.

The variation of the directional modulus ratios with elongation is a useful method of evaluating and expressing the anisotropic characteristics of the poromeric which in turn gives an indication of the lasting characteristics of the poromeric.

For the poromerics and leathers tested, elastic recovery and resilience at 10% extension is approximately proportional to the modulus at 10% extension.

Resilience measurements indicate no correlation with flex performance.

A useful method of assessing the properties of the poromeric is to compare the stress-strain curves for the individual layers with the curves for the complete poromeric. The difference between the first and subsequent extensions may also be of significance in determining the degree of mutual reinforcement provided by the layers.

REFERENCE

[1] *B.B.S.I. J.* **15**, 79 (1968).

ACKNOWLEDGEMENTS

The author wishes to express his thanks to Mr M. Endo, Manager of Planning, Hi-Telac Company Ltd, for all the experimental data provided.

CHAPTER 2

The Mullins effect and the set of poromerics

A. R. PAYNE and D. POPPLEWELL

INTRODUCTION

A PROGRAMME of work has been undertaken to investigate the mechanisms involved in straining and setting poromeric upper materials.

The first part of this paper discusses the results previously obtained with rubbers and other viscoelastic materials, and forms the background to the present studies.

The second part shows the similarity between the earlier studies on viscoelastic materials, and the present studies on leather and poromerics.

PART I

Shoemaking relies on the ability of the upper materials to be formed and shaped to take the form of the last on which the shoe is built up. This requires a certain degree of plastic-like behaviour in the material. There have been numerous studies on the various processes used with leather to produce this plasticity involving such techniques as heat setting and mulling with moisture. The newer synthetic upper materials, based on pvc, rely on the thermoplastic nature of the plastic to retain its last shape. On the other hand poromerics are new materials and have not been studied in depth.

This paper concerns itself with one aspect of 'plasticity' which has been well studied in the rubber industry and is known as the phenomenon of stress softening or the 'Mullins effect' [1] . It is shown here that the mechanical properties of both leather and poromerics do exhibit the Mullins effect phenomenon, and therefore a study of this phenomenon should lead to some understanding of the 'mechanics' involved in shoemaking with these materials.

Fig. 2.1 illustrates a hypothetical stress-strain curve; the stress-softening phenomenon is concerned with two aspects of this behaviour, firstly with the amount of energy lost at short times, and secondly with the amount of residual extension remaining after a period of time after the stress is removed.

It is possible for two completely different polymer systems to traverse the same stress-strain curve A B C during a stress-strain cycle; however, curve 1 will, after a period of time, completely return from point C to the origin with no residual set. Depending on the nature of

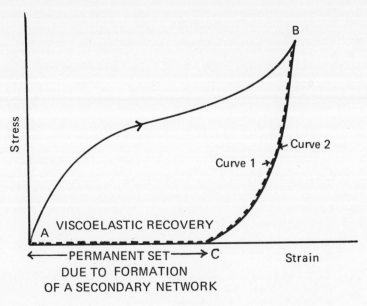

Fig. 2.1.

the viscoelastic response the time to complete recovery can be rapid
or can take place over many years. In the case of the long time recovery,
this can be speeded up by placing the sample in a higher temperature
environment or by swelling in a solvent.

However, in the second case, curve 2, complete recovery from point C
is not obtained. In rubber vulcanizates this lack of recovery can be
attributed to crosslinks being of the labile type, i.e. polysulphide,
organo-metallic complex crosslinks or pseudo crosslinks, such as
hydrogen bonds, or due to attractive forces between polyethylene
segments, say in a thermoplastic polymer. The ability of polymer
systems to retain high extensions when shaped depends therefore on
both the viscoelastic response of the base polymer and/or the presence
or absence of labile networks in the polymer or leather material.

THE MULLINS EFFECT—BACKGROUND STUDIES

A sample of rubber requires a greater stress to produce a given
elongation in its first extension than during subsequent extensions.
All rubbers, vulcanized or unvulcanized, filled or unfilled, exhibit this
phenomenon known as stress softening and it is illustrated by the
stress-strain curves in Fig. 2.2. If at point A on the first extension curve
OA the specimen is retracted to zero stress then the second extension
to a high strain is represented by curve OBAC and, after retraction, the
third extension to a still higher strain by curve ODCE. Clearly the first
and subsequent extension curves are markedly different.

Stress softening has been the subject of many experimental and
theoretical investigations and several mechanisms responsible for the
phenomenon have been proposed. The phenomenon was described in
1903 by Bouasse and Carriere [2], who in fact made reference to works as

20

early as 1880 and 1898. In 1910, Schwartz [3] measured energy losses by strain cycling filled rubbers and the increased extension attained in successive deformations by the same maximum load. The following year Beadle and Stevens [4], using a machine designed by Schwartz examined hysteresis properties of natural rubber (NR) vulcanizates containing different amounts of zinc oxide or talc. Their results showed stress-softening in gum vulcanizates as well as in filler loaded compounds. In 1922 Gurney and Travener [5] in the USA described the effect in filled compounds during an investigation of aircraft shock absorbers. Also in the USA Somerville and Cope [6] (1928) designed a machine to stretch rubber and simultaneously record the force-extension characteristics at various temperatures. They showed that, when

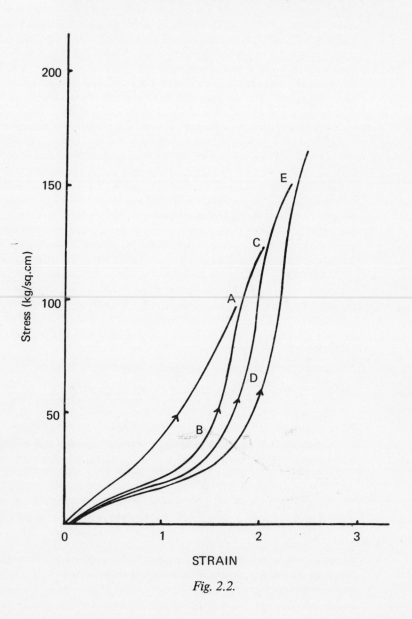

Fig. 2.2.

stretching NR gum vulcanizates to 500% strain, several cycles were required before the stress-strain curve was constant and the final curve was very different from that obtained initially. In 1931, Holt [7] showed a softening effect in NR gum vulcanizates stretched up to 700% elongation and also in tyre tread vulcanizates. He also demonstrated that partial recovery was possible by allowing the softening samples to remain at room temperature for 24 hours.

No theoretical explanations were forthcoming from these early investigations and it was 1947 before work carried out by Mullins [8, 9, 10], was sufficiently quantitative for theoretical considerations to be attempted. He showed that stress softening was usually only present at strains less than the previous maximum strain and by applying corrections for permanent set to the softened stress-strain curves he deduced that stress softening in NR gum vulcanizates was negligible. These experimental contributions led to the description of the phenomenon of stress softening in filler-loaded rubbers as the 'Mullins effect'. Later work by Mullins and Tobin concentrated on softening effects in filled vulcanizates. They considered filled rubber as a heterogeneous system comprising hard and soft phases. Blanchard and Parkinson [11, 12] attributed the Mullins effect, or stress softening, to the breakage of rubber-to-filler attachments rather than to particle-to-particle cohesions. However, measurements of the temperature rise on cycling samples of filled rubber led Marshall *et al.* [13], to conclude that . . . 'over 90% of the energy used in softening rubber appears as heat and this places a limit on the energy available for breaking chemical bonds or for effecting a change of state in the rubber . . .'

Bueche [14, 15, 16] distinguished between changes in gum rubbers and softening in filler-loaded rubbers. He showed that the changes in gum rubbers due to viscously retarded rubber networks are recoverable in the majority of cases but he attributed the permanent softening in filled rubbers to breakage of rubber-filled bonds. He described the latter effect in terms of a molecular theory which assumes that the filler particles are displaced affinely during deformations of the rubber. He considered that chains connected at both ends to filler particles will break when the separation of the particles is sufficient to stretch the chains to near full elongation.

The most recent investigations of stress softening are those of:

1 Dannenberg, Boonstra and co-workers [17, 18, 19, 20], who envisage a slippage of the rubber network chains over the surface of the filler particles.
2 Kraus *et al.* [21], who consider the effect to be the result of several mechanisms: thixotropy involving transient carbon black structures, rupture of network chains connecting filler particles and disruption of the 'permanent structure' of the carbon black.
3 Harwood and Payne [22, 23, 24, 25], who claim that most of the stress softening occurs in the gum phase of the filled vulcanizate leaving little to be explained in terms of breakage or slippage of rubber-to-filler bonds.

From these investigations it is certain that stress softening can result from one or more of several mechanisms and these are briefly summarized as follows:

1 Rearrangement of the rubber network associated with slippage of entanglements and non-affine displacement of network junctions in the rubber matrix. This occurs in gum vulcanizates and in the gum phase of filled vulcanizates.
2 Structural changes of the carbon black aggregates. This is associated with the possible breakdown and reformation of filler 'domains', or breakage of the 'permanent' structure of the carbon black particles. The latter mechanism was suggested by Kraus and others but no independent evidence of this mechanism has been presented.
3 Slippage of rubber chains on the black surface or the breakage of rubber-filler bonds. These are involved in the Dannenberg-Boonstra and Bueche theories respectively but there is no independent evidence of these mechanisms.
4 Breakage of weak crosslinks such as hydrogen bonds, ionic type links and polysulphide links.
5 Displacement of large particles through the rubber matrix: hydrodynamic effects.

In gum vulcanizates containing stable crosslinks, stress softening can be completely recovered by heating or swelling, but in filled rubbers stress softening is only partially recovered. This non-recovery need not reflect a breakage or slippage of rubber-filled attachments but simply the inability of the large filler particles, perhaps to some extent reaggregated, to return to their initial state.

From consideration of the energy changes associated with stress softening, mechanisms (1) and (2) together with (4) for rubbers with weak crosslinks, almost entirely account for the energy losses in filler-loaded vulcanizates. The other mechanisms are speculative and at most only account for a small fraction of the energy losses in the stress-softening process.

The suggested mechanism of slipping crosslinks or breakage of rubber-black linkages is not essential to account for a lack of complete recovery, as the presence of secondary networks due to labile crosslinks, or a reformed aggregated structure of carbon black also prevent complete recovery of the stress-softening process. Carbon black results in an enhancement of actual strain in the rubber phase and this leads to an increase in energy losses at a given strain.

Recent papers by Grosch, Harwood and Payne [26, 27] have shown how the energy at break of a rubber vulcanizate is directly related to the hysteresis in the polymer at failure. It was found that the toughest polymers, i.e. those that withstood the greatest energy input, were those which exhibited the largest hysteresis and the largest stress softening. Now because toughness, or strength, depends upon hysteresis, the concept of stress softening takes on a new significance and it is important to consider both the irrecoverable and recoverable contributions to stress softening together, in contrast to the ideas of Bueche and Kraus.

A MODEL FOR THE MULLINS EFFECT

Fig. 2.3 is a photograph of a network of string. Knots have been tied between two pieces of string so that the knot acts as a tetrafunctional

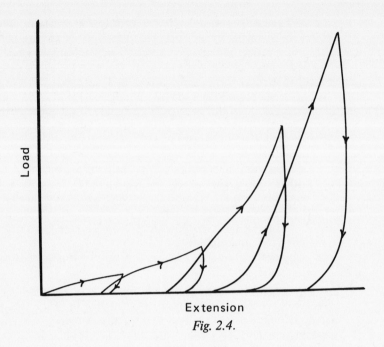

Fig. 2.4.

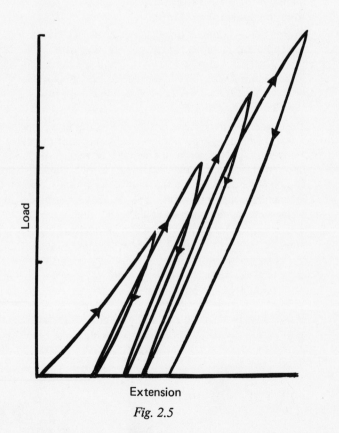

Fig. 2.5

crosslink point. The lengths of string between the knots are randomly
varied, so that some pieces of string between 'crosslinks' are short, others
are quite lengthy. This model is inserted between pins attached to
the jaws of the Instron Tensile Testing Machine, and the 'knotted'
network of string is then stress cycled in the same manner as described
earlier for the stress cycling of rubber.

Fig. 2.4 is a typical set of curves resulting from this experiment and
quite clearly reproduces some of the features characteristic of the
Mullins effect.

STRESS SOFTENING IN LEATHER

There was little evidence in the literature that the Mullins effect
existed for leather, except for one diagrammatic curve for fibres of

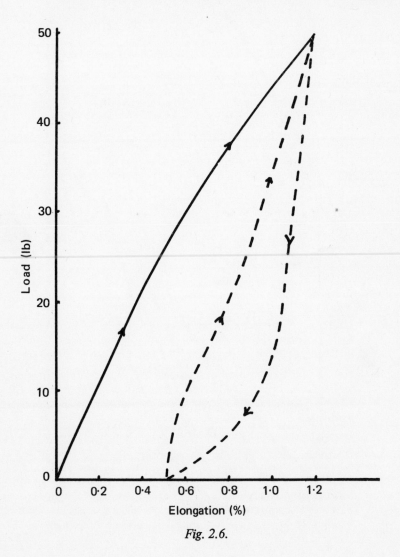

Fig. 2.6.

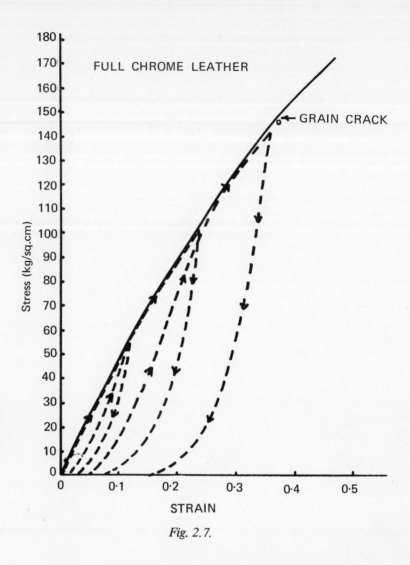

FULL CHROME LEATHER

GRAIN CRACK

Fig. 2.7.

leather which Mitton [28] had published, and which is reproduced in Fig. 2.5, and a curve produced by Maeser [29] shown in Fig. 2.6. These sequences of curves clearly show a 'Mullins' stress-softening effect.

Fig. 2.7 is a stress cycling sequence carried out on a full-chrome leather tested on the Instron. Quite clearly the Mullins effect or stress-softening effect is present, and therefore we must regard leather in this respect like a polymer.

Leather, although chemically modified by the tanning process, is still essentially a natural product like cotton or wool, and like these two materials reacts in a special way to moisture and heat. Jackson [30] has described in a recent review paper how leather is composed of a network of interlaced protein (collagen) fibres which are made up of various interconnected sub-units. On a molecular scale, the basic collagen 'building block' is a helical bundle composed of three chains of molecules twisted round each other, like the strands of rope, as shown in Fig. 2.8.

These bundles make up 'protofibrils' and the 'filaments'. Filaments in turn made up 'fibrils' (Fig. 2.9) which form complete fibres. In addition to the molecular bonds connecting the molecules in the fundamental chains, other bonds, known as 'hydrogen bonds', tie the chains, bundles, protofibrils, filaments, fibrils and fibres together. These bonds are not as strong as the molecular links in the chains, but they do provide sufficient cross-ties between the sub-units.

The hydrogen bonds are essentially weak bonds and in the presence of moisture, rupture of the interchain H-bonds occurs in the manner shown in Fig. 2.10 with the consequence that there is no freedom of relative movement between the chains when subjected to mechanical shearing stresses. On drying or in an extended or distorted condition, there is reformation of the interchain H-bonds and a new secondary network is thereby produced. This behaviour is analogous to the labile crosslinks of a polysulphide crosslinked vulcanizate of, for instance, natural rubber or styrene-butadiene rubber (SBR) and has been the study of many theoretical and experimental investigations.

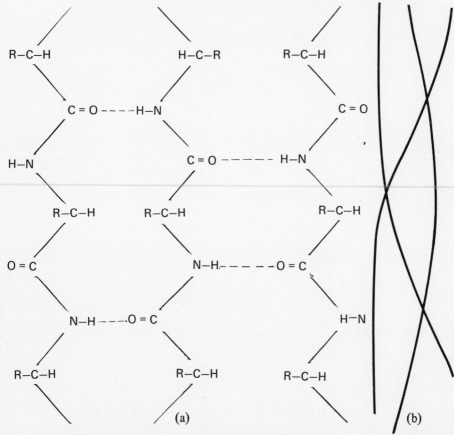

Fig. 2.8. (a) Shows a schematic representation of three protein chains linked by hydrogen bonding; (b) in collagen the protein chains are twisted around each other in the form of a three stranded rope.

27

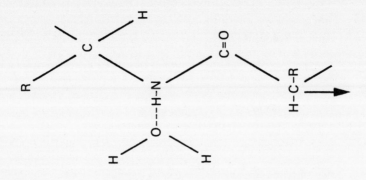

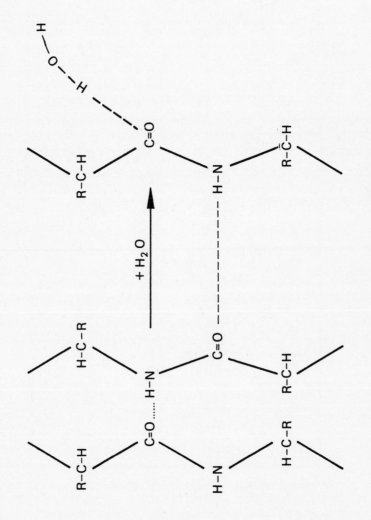

Fig. 2.10.

28

Quite clearly, mechanical stressing can bring about stress softening, but the presence of moisture, a highly hysteretic fibrilant system, possibly even Coulombian friction between crossed fibrils, can help to bring about a situation which allows for a high set to be obtained. However, a deeper discussion on the properties of leather is the subject for other publications.

STRESS SOFTENING IN A POROMERIC

Fig. 2.11 illustrates the stress-softening curve for an experimental poromeric, a poromeric which is a polyurethane and does not contain any fibre reinforcements. Again the 'Mullins' effect is apparent. The energy losses are associated with the movement of polymer chains, crosslinks and entanglement points when the poromeric is stressed. The set resulting is the result of two phenomena:

1 The viscoelastic nature of the polyurethane molecule, which exhibits a very wide distribution of relaxation times, especially in the rubbery plateau region, the intensity of the relaxation

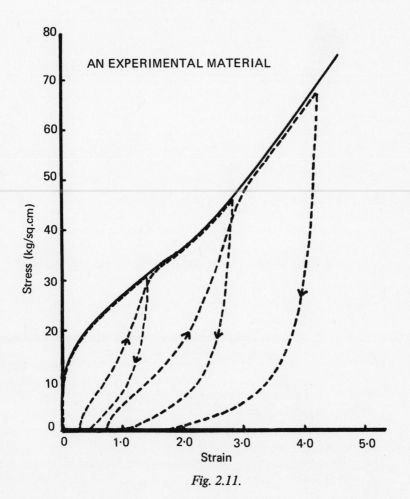

Fig. 2.11.

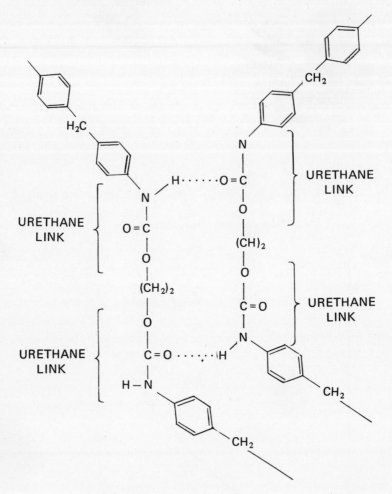

Fig. 2.12. Chains showing sites for —H ----- O = bridges.

distribution is both high and very wide. This means that recovery from a prestressing is a long time process.

2 The presence of hydrogen bonds between neighbouring chains. These bonds can break under mechanical stress and in the presence of moisture in the same way as the interchain H-bonds, discussed above for leather.

Fig. 2.12 illustrates a typical polyurethane backbone linked with a hydrogen bond.

The Mullins effect in polyurethane has been noted in the literature by Trick [31].

PART II

BEHAVIOUR OF POROMERICS

Individual poromerics can differ very widely from each other; some of them can have very complex structures, but most, if not all of them, contain large proportions of polyurethane, which is a viscoelastic material.

Corfam is made up of three distinct layers: a polyurethane foam layer, a woven fabric interlayer, and a non-woven base layer (see Fig. 2.13). The foam layer has a top skin of polyurethane and nitrocellulose which forms the protective outer coat of the material, but it will have negligible effect on the mechanical properties and so is not considered further.

The fabric interlayer can be seen in Fig. 2.13 as an undulating bundle of fibres just under the top layer. The circular bundles are the opposite weave coming out of the plane of the paper. The threads in the interlayer are composed mainly of polyester fibres with a little cotton.

The base layer consists of a dense mass of randomly orientated polyester fibres which are held together by polyurethane binder.

From the structure of Corfam we would expect it to have a comparatively high modulus, i.e. rather 'tight' in shoemaking terms, due to the presence of the fabric interlayer and the dense non-woven base.

In contrast, Clarino (see Fig. 2.14) consists basically of two layers. The foam layer is very similar to that of Corfam except that the top skin appears to be composed entirely of polyurethane.

Clarino contains no fabric interlayer and the base layer appears to be less dense than that of Corfam. The number of fibres seems to be much less while the proportion of binder is far greater.

From a knowledge of the structures we would expect Clarino to have a lower modulus and be more extensible than Corfam, as the restrictive fabric interlayer is absent.

A section through the thickness of leather (Fig. 2.15) shows that the traditional shoemaking material consists almost entirely of a fibrous structure, although it is true that the fibres tend to be finer in the top (grain) layer. The randomly orientated fibres branch and rejoin forming a continuous three-dimensional network without the need for any supporting binder as in a man-made poromeric.

The influence the structure has on the stress-strain properties of shoe materials is shown in Fig. 2.16 in which three poromerics are compared with leather. The leather used was a full chrome side leather and hence it has a rather high modulus. The term leather covers materials with nearly as wide a range of properties as does poromerics. Thus, this cannot be regarded as a unique curve for leather but it does give an indication of how poromerics compare with a tight side leather. The curves in Fig. 2.16 have been made up from two separate tests. One sample was strained to break, and a second sample was returned to zero just before failure to show the retraction curve.

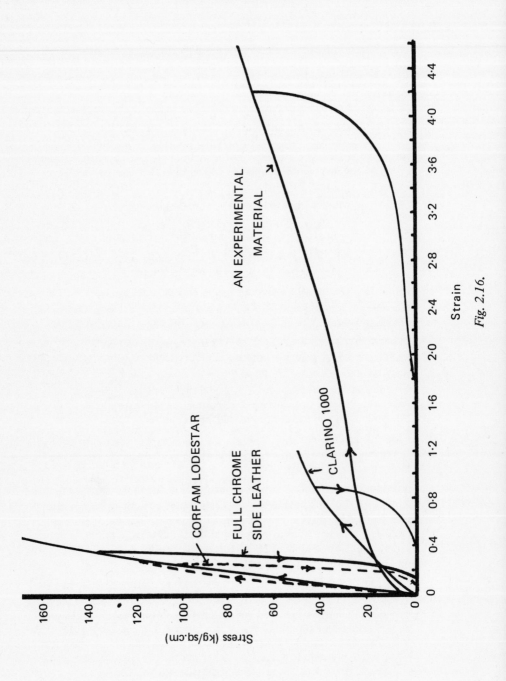

Fig. 2.16.

32

The differences in the stresses and strains at break can be clearly seen in the diagram, but they are summarized below in Table 2.1.

Table 2.1

| Material | Values at break | |
	Stress kg/cm^2	% Extension
Corfam*	120	28
Clarino	50	120
Experimental material	75	456
Leather	175	48

* Failure of fabric interlayer.

The breaking stresses vary from 50 kg/cm^2 to 175 kg/cm^2 and the breaking extension from 28% to over 450%. It is interesting to note that all these materials have been successfully made into shoes, which shows the remarkable versatility of shoemakers and shoe machinery.

The difference between the stress-strain and retraction curves, for the three poromerics taken to a constant load is shown in Fig. 2.17. Side leather has not been included in this diagram because the curves for side leather and Corfam are identical under these conditions.

It is seen that Corfam, the tightest material, has a low hysteresis (the area enclosed by the extension and retraction curves which can be used to calculate the energy absorbed during a strain cycle). Clarino has a much lower modulus and a large hysteresis value. The very extensible experimental material has also a large hysteresis value.

If we next compare the materials taken to a constant strain of 10% (Fig. 2.18) we see that at these low extensions Corfam has the highest modulus, with Clarino (not shown) and the experimental material the lowest. Incidentally, the modulus of the materials at these low extensions can be relevant in foot comfort considerations, as it gives an indication of the ability of the material to accommodate foot abnormalities such as bunions.

THE MULLINS EFFECT

The Mullins or stress-softening effect has been seen earlier to be present in single layer materials; Fig. 2.19 shows it to be present in Corfam. The dotted line is the tensile curve for Corfam taken to the break of the fabric interlayer. The continuous curves are for a second sample which was initially strained to a fixed extension, the direction of the motion of the jaws was then reversed. When the jaws had returned to their original position of zero extension the same sample was again extended. It can be seen from Fig. 2.19 that on the second extension the stress for a given

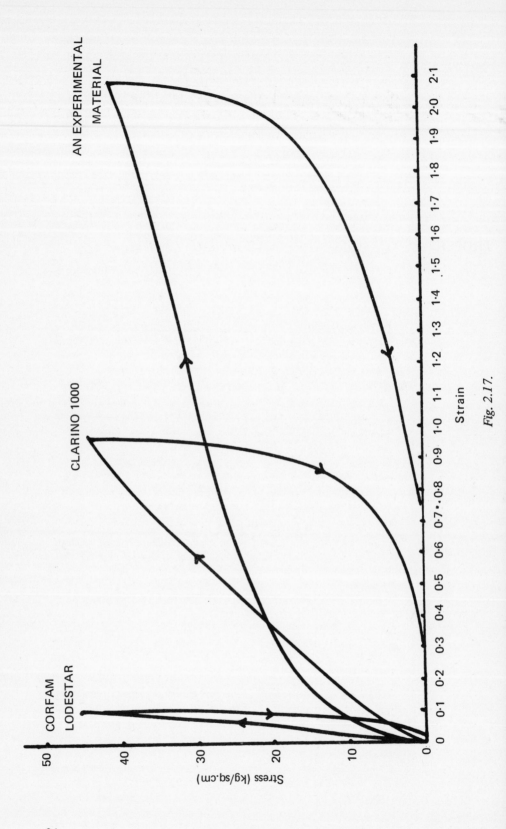

Fig. 2.17.

34

strain is always less than on the first until the maximum extension in the first cycle is reached. If the loading is then continued the curve for the second sample approximates very closely to that for the tensile specimen. If the direction of motion of the jaws is again reversed back to the zero position and the sample strained for a third time the same phenomenon is observed, namely a lower stress for a given strain up to the maximum extension on the second cycle after which there is again coincidence with the tensile sample.

A similar stress-softening effect is observed with Clarino up to a maximum extension of 120% and the experimental material (already referred to) up to a maximum extension of over 400% (see Figs. 2.20 and 2.11 respectively).

PROPERTIES OF THE DIFFERENT LAYERS

The stress-softening effect shown for rubbers has also been seen to occur with poromerics, which, as pointed out earlier, are based on viscoelastic polyurethane materials. But, in contrast to rubber, these materials are non-uniform through their structures. Corfam has three distinct layers, the top foam layer, the fabric interlayer and the

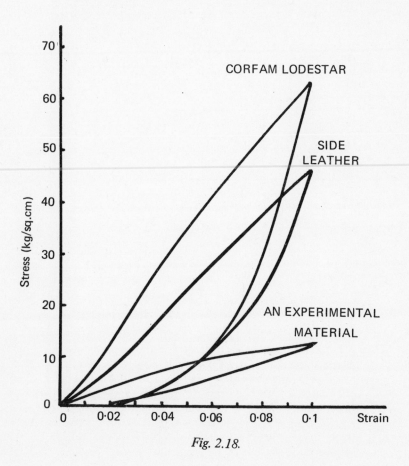

Fig. 2.18.

35

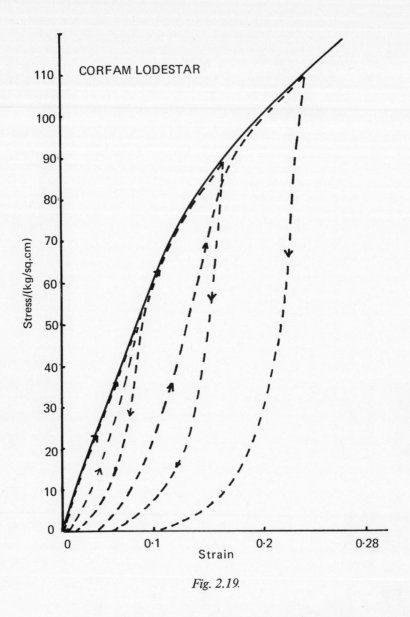

Fig. 2.19.

non-woven base layer, each of which has a different structure and thus can be expected to have different stress-strain properties.

The stress-strain curves to break for the different layers of Corfam (Fig. 2.21) illustrates the difference in these properties. The tight fabric interlayer has a high stress and low strain at break, while the base layer has a higher extension (80%) and much lower stress at break. The foam polyurethane layer has a very low modulus and high extension at break. If we compare the three layers at a constant extension of 10% (see Fig. 2.22) we see that at this extension the fabric interlayer takes the largest proportion of the load. It shows a high hysteresis (energy loss) and has the highest set of the three components. The base layer takes a smaller proportion of the load and has the lowest set of the three layers. The top layer can be seen to contribute little to the load bearing properties of the material. If the stresses at equal strains are summed for the three layers it can be seen that there is reasonably good agreement with the curve for an intact sample tested under the same conditions. Thus in Corfam at least, there appears to be very little interaction between the layers. It is hoped to be able to study each layer independently and sum the results to get an indication of the properties of the whole material. This might be necessary as when materials are strained in a shoe, the upper is often strained by bending, thus the extension is not uniform through the thickness. The extent of the

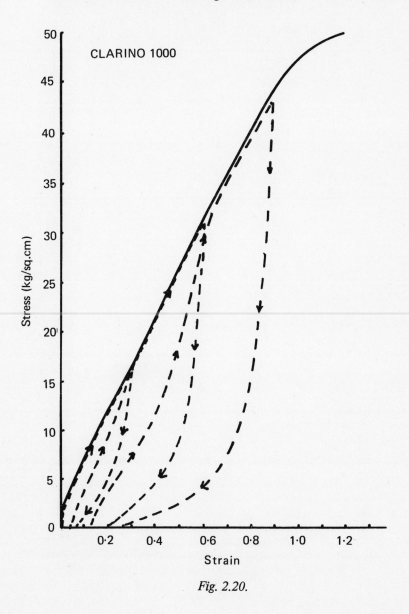

Fig. 2.20.

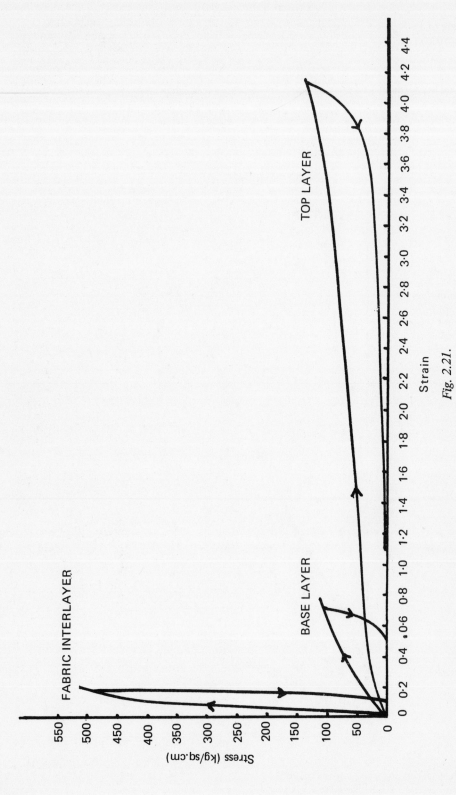

Fig. 2.21.

PLATE 3

Fig. 3.1. Natural leather.
480 x magnification

Fig. 3.2. A cross-section of a poromeric
showing: base layer, fabric layer
and microporous layer.
116 x magnification

Fig. 3.3. Detail of microporous binder
and fibres in a base layer.
480 x magnification

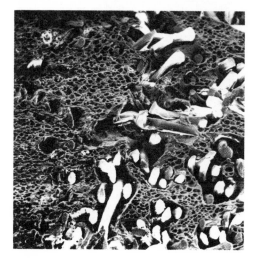

PLATE 4

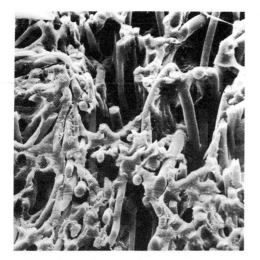

Fig. 3.4. Detail of solid binder and fibres in a base layer.
480 x magnification

Fig. 3.5. Detail of microporous binder and a blend of fibres in the base layer.
480 x magnification

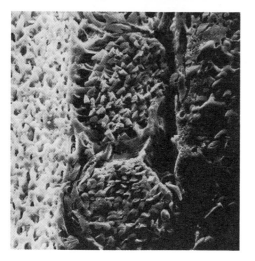

Fig. 3.6. Separate microporous layer for the woven fabric layer.
480 x magnification

PLATE 5

Fig. 3.7. Fabric layer imbedded in the top microporous layer.
480 x magnification

Fig. 3.8. Fabric embedded in microporous polymer continuous throughout the poromeric.
480 x magnification

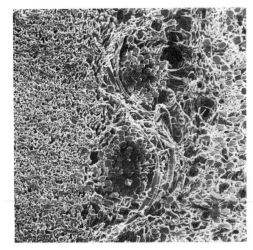

Fig. 3.9. A microporous layer with few large closed cells.
450 x magnification

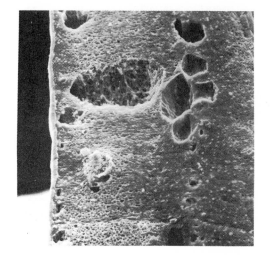

PLATE 6

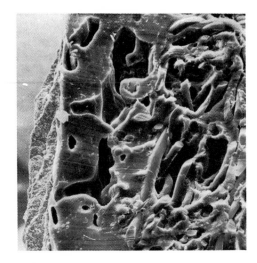

Fig. 3.10. A microporous layer with large open pores.
480 x magnification

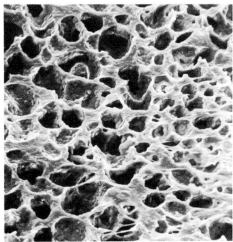

Fig. 3.11. Small semi-closed cell type of microporous layer.
4,480 x magnification

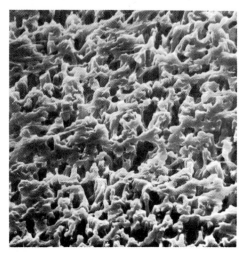

Fig. 3.12. Small inter-connecting cell type of microporous layer.
8,800 x magnification

PLATE 7

Fig. 3.13. Small/large inter-connecting cell type of microporous layer.
480 x magnification

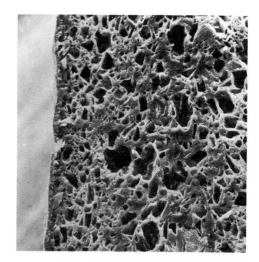

Fig. 3.14. Small/large cell structure with embedded fibres.
480 x magnification

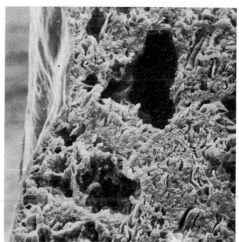

Fig. 3.15. Thin solid layer in microporous structure causing low permeability.
480 x magnification

PLATE 8

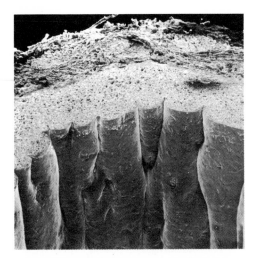

Fig. 3.16. Surface and cross-section of a poromeric folded at "break" conditions.
96 x magnification

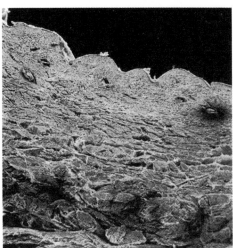

Fig. 3.17. Cross-section showing "break" in natural leather.
120 x magnification

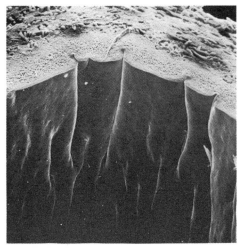

Fig. 3.18. Deep folds in a poromeric "break".
90 x magnification

PLATE 9

Fig. 3.19. Open fold in a poromeric "break". 2,800 x magnification

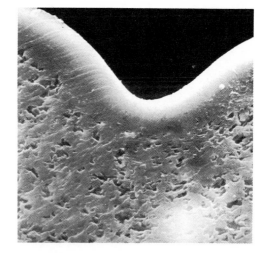

Fig. 3.20. Detail of a deep fold in a poromeric "break". 380 x magnification

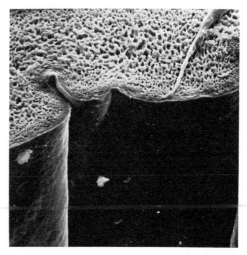

Fig. 3.21. Ridges formed after 1 pass during snag test. 114 x magnification

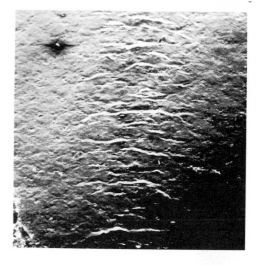

PLATE 10

Fig. 3.22. Initial breakdown of surface finish.
112 x magnification

Fig. 3.23. Final breakdown of the surface finish.
110 x magnification

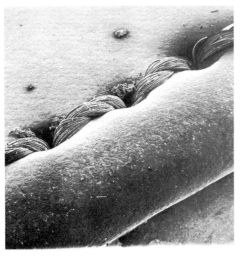

Fig. 3.24. Stitching along a beaded edge.
48 x magnification`

extension of the grain layer depends upon the position of the neutral axis for a given degree of folding.

CONCLUSION

The first part of this paper described the 'Mullins' effect and its applicability to rubbers, plastics, wool fibres, poromerics and leather. Also discussed were the reasons for the presence of set in viscoelastic materials, as well as the ways in which set in a material such as rubber or polyurethane can be made permanent by the introduction of labile linkages into the polymer network. Labile bonds break as the material is extended and reform when it is held in a strained state for a short time, thereby introducing a new secondary network into the material and producing a real permanent set in contrast to the normal slow recovery manifested as a temporary set.

In the second part the stress-strain properties of several poromerics were shown and an indication given of how the properties of the whole sample depended on the various layers. There appears to be a close similarity between the stress-softening phenomenon observed for poromerics and for rubbers, leather, plastics and wool. We should, therefore, be able to make use of the previous research work into polymer network structures in order to obtain a better understanding of

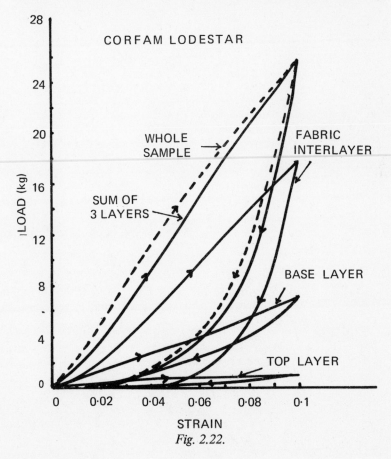

Fig. 2.22.

the mechanisms involved when a poromeric is strained and in this way be able to make recommendations for the development of even better materials for shoemaking.

REFERENCES

1   Harwood, J. A. C., Mullins, L., and Payne, A. R. *J. IRI* (1967), **1**, 1.
2   Bouasse, H., and Carriere, Z. *Annales de la Faculté des Sciences de Toulouse* (1903), **5**, 257.
3   Schwartz, A. *J. Inst. Elec. Eng.* (London) (1910), **44**, 693.
4   Beadle, C., and Stevens, H. P. *J. Chem. Soc.* (1911), **30**, 1 421.
5   Gurney, H. P., and Travener, C. H. *Ind. Eng. Chem.* (1922), **14**, 134.
6   Somerville, A. A., and Cope, W. H. *Trans. IRI* (1928), **4**, 263.
7   Holt, W. L. *Ind. Eng. Chem.* (1931), **23**, 1 471.
8   Mullins, L. *J. Rubb. Res.* (1947), **16**, 275.
9   Mullins, L. *J. Phys. and Coll. Chem.* (1950), **54**, 239.
10   Mullins, L., and Tobin, N. R. *Proc. Third Rubb. Tech. Conf.* (London, 1954), (1956), 397.
11   Blanchard, A. F., and Parkinson, D. *Ind. Eng. Chem.* (1952), **44**, 799.
12   Blanchard, A. F., *J. Polym. Sci.* (1954), **14**, 355.
13   Marshall, D. G., Walker, D. L., and Smith, J. G. *Rubb. Chem. Tech.* (1955), **28**, 1 123.
14   Bueche, F. *J. Appl. Polym. Sci.* (1961), **5**, 271.
15   Bueche, F. *J. Appl. Polym. Sci.* (1960), **4**, 107.
16   Bueche, F. *Reinforcement of Elastomers,* ed. G. Kraus (1965), Interscience, New York, Chap. 1.
17   Dannenberg, E. M. *Trans. IRI* (1966), **42**, T26.
18   Boonstra, B. B. *Reinforcement of Elastomers,* ed. G. Kraus, (1965), Interscience, New York, Chap. 16:
19   Dannenberg, E. M., and Brennan, J. J. *ACS Div. Rubb. Chem.,* Philadelphia, Oct. 1965, Paper No. 22.
20   Brennan, J. J., Jermyn, T. E., and Perdagio, M. F. *ACS Div. Rubb. Chem.,* Detroit, May 1964, Paper No. 36.
21   Kraus, G., Childers, C. W., and Rollman, K. W. *J. Appl. Polym. Sci.* (1966), **10**, 229.
22   Harwood, J. A. C., Mullins, L., and Payne, A. R. *J. Appl. Polym. Sci.* (1965), **9**, 3 011.
23   Harwood, J. A. C., and Payne, A. R. *J. Appl. Polym. Sci.* (1966), **10**, 315.
24   Harwood, J. A. C., and Payne, A. R. *J. Appl. Polym. Sci.* (1966), **10**, 1 203.
25   Harwood, J. A. C., and Payne, A. R. *Trans. IRI* (1966), **42**, T14.
26   Grosch, K., Harwood, J. A. C., and Payne, A. R. *Nature* (1966), **212**, 497.
27   Grosch, K., Harwood, J. A. C., and Payne, A. R. Paper read to Inst. of Physics Conf., *The Physical Basis of Yield and Fracture,* Oxford, Sept. 1966.
28   Mitton, R. G. *J. SLTC* (1945), **29**, 169.
29   Maeser, M. *The Chemistry and Technology of Leather,* ed. O'Flaherty, Roddy and Lollar, Reinhold, New York, **4**, Chap. 62.
30   Jackson, E. G. *Tech. J. Nat. Footwear Manufacturers Assn.,* **4**, No. 4, March 1968, 130.
31   Trick, G. S. *J. Appl. Polym. Sci.* (1960), **3**, 252.

CHAPTER 3

Aspects of the structure of poromerics

A. J. SHERRIN and Dr. J. W. WATSON

INTRODUCTION

POROMERICS are a new range of useful materials and to understand precisely how they behave, it is important to understand their structure. It is necessary to know the behaviour of poromerics during service life and during shoe manufacture. At the production stage, it is also important to be able to relate structure to physical properties as well as to determine the effect of product development and process changes.

Over a period of years the detailed structure of the whole range of tanned hides has been carefully studied. It can now be said that these structures are basically well understood. The study of poromerics, however, presents a rather different problem because, although their whole 'raison d'être' is to have 'leather-like' qualities, their detailed structure is very different from those of natural hides.

Generally, poromerics are composite materials consisting of polymers and fibres. It is found that these structures are not easy to study in detail by the usual analytical techniques. It is possible to obtain some general information by use of infra-red spectroscopy and standard fibre methods, which give information on the type of the polymer and fibres and perhaps the construction of the fibre regions. However, in addition to these valuable techniques, we have recently been able to apply certain modern methods of microscopy to study these materials. It is largely evidence from this recent work that is presented in the paper.

MICROSCOPY

The structure of tanned and untanned natural hides was largely established by light microscope methods which led to a better understanding of the many variations that occur in natural hides. These methods are not easily applied to poromerics because thin sections are difficult to cut and the light microscope is not an ideal instrument for examining cross-sections of porous materials. The conventional transmission electron microscope has its limitations as the structure of poromerics is usually too coarse for this refined technique. In recent years, the new technique of scanning electron microscopy has been developed and has now been used for examining poromerics. The microscope used in these investigations is the Stereoscan, manufactured by Cambridge Scientific Instrument Co.

The Stereoscan uses a new approach to microscopy in which the surface of the specimen is examined directly A focused beam of electrons scans the surface of the specimen which emits a signal consisting of scattered secondary electrons; this signal is collected and fed through a series of amplifiers to produce a magnified image displayed on a cathode-ray tube. One of the advantages is that the specimen surface is examined directly without the need for complicated replicas or thin sections which often contain artefacts. The Stereoscan has a depth of field between 300-1000 times better than the conventional light microscope and has a magnification range from 20 times to over 30000 times with a resolving power of 300 Å. The specimens are mounted directly on ½-in. diameter aluminium stubs which are placed directly in the instrument. It is possible to examine in clear detail, by this technique, porous structures, fibre composites, rough surfaces, fracture surfaces, etc, without the 'out of focus blur' which is evident with most light microscope images of surfaces. A good example is shown in Fig. 3.1 which shows a detail of the Corium in a cross-section of a tanned side leather.

Poromerics are usually non-conducting specimens and need to be coated with a thin film (150-200 Å) of conducting metal, e.g. platinum, to prevent surface charging. This film, of course, is too fine to be visible on the final image. By taking two successive images of the same specimen at different angles, it is possible to produce stereoscopic pairs which show the structure in its true depth, making it possible to determine the precise position of each part of the structure.

STRUCTURE OF POROMERICS

There are a number of poromerics currently available which show a wide variety of structures and some examples of these will be discussed. Apart from the basic construction of the poromeric, the Stereoscan can be used to show how these structures behave under certain circumstances. In particular, examples of surface 'break', abrasion, surface finish, beaded edge and stitching have been examined. This list is by no means exhaustive but the results gained so far will be of some interest.

It is widely known that poromerics are usually two or three layer structures which comprise a microporous top sheet, sometimes a fabric layer, and fibre base. The so-called modulus poromerics have an interlayer and the low modulus materials have none.

BASE LAYER

The base layer is usually the thickest part of a poromeric structure being one-half to two-thirds of the total thickness. This is a fundamental part of any poromeric and governs much of its gross properties of strength, flexibility, water vapour adsorption, etc.

The base of most poromerics consists of a random fibre complex with a polymer binder. The fibres are usually short fine-denier staple and can be a blend of different types. These base felts are often needled to give vertical as well as horizontal entanglements and this can clearly be seen in some specimens. There are, however, detailed aspects of the base which vary: firstly the concentration of the fibres, and secondly the type and distribution of binder material. The structures vary from those containing a high concentration of fibres with a little solid binder as shown in Fig. 3.2, to those containing a few fibres with a large volume of microporous binder, as shown in Fig. 3.3. Between these two extremes are a number of variations.

Because the base layer is on the inside of the shoe, it is dominant in a poromeric's water vapour adsorption (WVA). There are many factors which influence the WVA of a poromeric, such as the type of fibres used in the base and the fabric, but from our observations there appears to be a structural factor. Those poromerics which have a large free volume or exposed free surface in their base layers tend to have a high WVA (1·8–4·0) (Fig. 3.4) but the poromerics which have a high proportion of closed-cell microporous binder in the base tend to have lower WVA (1·0–1·3) (Fig. 3.5). The closed-cell structure presumably cuts down the amount of free volume surface available for WVA.

FABRIC INTERLAYER

There are some interesting differences between fabric layers of the high modulus materials involving variations in the fabric itself, i.e. weave, fibre, yarn denier, etc., but most obvious are the ways in which the fabric is bonded to the rest of the structure.

The three most common ways are as follows.
(a) The fabric having a separate microporous binder (Fig. 3.6)
(b) The fabric is embedded in the microporous top sheet (Fig. 3.7)
(c) The fabric is embedded in the microporous material which is continuous throughout the poromeric (Fig. 3.8).

No direct influence on physical properties could be attributed to these various bonding systems, but it is possible that combined with the structure of the fabric they have an effect on flexibility, modulus and other properties.

MICROPOROUS TOP SHEET

The microporous layer is an important part in a poromeric as it is the detailed structure of this layer which defines most of the subtle 'leather-like' qualities of poromerics. The microporous layer in combination with a finish layer is responsible for such properties as appearance, air permeability, water vapour permeability, 'break', abrasion resistance, flexing, etc. The structure of the microporous layer varies considerably from the almost solid structure with a few large closed-cells (see Fig. 3.9), and a small proportion of microporous structures to those with large open pores (see Fig. 3.10). The former material has a water vapour permeability of 0·4 and the latter a WVP of 3. These are not representative of most poromerics which lie between these two extremes. (All WVP data refer to the complete finished poromerics.)

Detailed analysis of the microporous layers of a range of poromerics show that there are three types of system commonly used:

(a) Small semi-closed cell
(b) small interconnecting cell, and
(c) small/large interconnecting cell.

(a) SMALL SEMI-CLOSED CELL (see Fig. 3.11)

The small semi-closed cell type has a high concentration of small closed voids (2-12μ diameter) and very thin separating walls (0·5μ thick). There appear to be few direct paths between the base and the surface and so some of the water vapour must be transmitted by a series of membrane transitions. It is noticeable that the WVP of the poromeric materials of this type were on average at the lower end of the range.

(b) SMALL INTERCONNECTING CELL (see Fig. 3.12)

The small interconnecting cell type has a high proportion of polymer-void ratio although the voids are of a similar size (5-12μ) to type (a). The thickness of the polymer struts is larger (2-5μ) and there are more obvious pathways between the base and the surface for water vapour to pass. Poromeric materials with this type of structure typically have WVP values higher than those in type (a).

(c) SMALL/LARGE INTERCONNECTING CELL STRUCTURE (see Fig. 3.13)

There were a number of wide variations in this type of structure, the extremes being illustrated by Figs. 3.13 and 3.14. Generally the small voids averaged 6μ in diameter and the large ones ranged from 20-120μ. In most cases the large voids were interconnected by the smaller ones which provide obvious pathways from the base to the surface of the material and as a class these poromeric materials had the highest WVP's. There was an unusual exception to this in a material of this type which had a WVP as low as 0·4 (see Fig. 3.15). Closer examination showed that there was a continuous solid polymer layer near the woven fabric area which obviously lowered the WVP considerably. We have no information if this was typical of the product as a whole or if it was only present in the sample which was examined. This, however, illustrates the usefulness of the Stereoscan for structural analysis.

Added to these types of cell structure were two or three examples of structures which have fine staple fibre added (see Fig. 3.14). These fibres may be present for a variety of reasons and it would be difficult to come to any real conclusion at this stage.

STRUCTURAL BEHAVIOUR OF POROMERIC MATERIALS

Although poromeric structures are interesting studies in their own right they are specifically intended for making into shoes and other useful articles. In use, therefore, they are flexed, bent, scuffed, stitched, etc., which means that the material needs to possess the right behaviour characteristics for its chosen purpose. It has been possible to study the behaviour of poromeric structures under a few of these all-important conditions. In particular 'break' and abrasion have been examined as well as some examples of stitched materials.

SURFACE 'BREAK'

'Break' is usually referred to as a desirable appearance factor. In reality it is the ability of the surface finish to produce a carefully controlled buckling so that a tight fold can occur without producing a single catastrophic crease. This is a highly complex phenomenon involving the bending of flexible beams and each part of the structure has its particular part to play. It is not possible in this context to give a complete explanation of 'break', but rather to show how structural behaviour can influence the 'break' in poromeric materials.

When a poromeric material is folded to produce a surface break (see Fig. 3.16) the base of the material is placed under tension while the surface is under compression. The material in the base will consolidate because of the tensile forces and this tends to stiffen the base. The surface is under compression and is being forced to occupy a smaller area and to contain this the surface arranges itself into a series of folds. It is the ability of leather and poromerics to control this incipient buckling that produces 'break'.

There are two extreme possibilities: either the whole material remains rigid, which produces the undesirable smooth surface finish, or the top surface collapses under compression and the base extends under tension to produce a single catastrophic crease. In the more normal situations, as the material is bent the surface begins to buckle in a number of places at fairly regular intervals. There is a whole range typically shown by the fine 'break' of a high quality calf to the pipey structure of a thick side leather.

It was observed, however, that there are two distinct differences in the type of indentations produced by poromeric materials. The 'break' of a high quality natural leather produces a series of fine indentations in the surface (see Fig. 3.17) but the actual indentations are held open and do not fold completely. This type of 'break' is also typical of some poromerics but in others the indentations penetrate deeply into the surface layer and produce a miniature fold (see Fig. 3.18). It appears that open indentations are formed when the surface finish can only produce a relatively small penetration of the underlying structure. This underlying structure then resists any further penetration as in natural leather.

In poromeric materials with open identations in their 'break' structures this resistance is achieved by various means. Fig. 3.19 shows the top layer to be under compression and further penetration is prevented by the relatively compact microporous layer. Where the folded indentations are too deep, the microporous layer is often of the small semi-closed cell type (see Fig. 3.20). In these folds the underlying structure is not compressed sufficiently to resist penetration.

45

This is obviously not the whole story as the relative physical properties of the surface finish, the microporous layer and the fibre base are also important.

SNAG TEST

In the SATRA standard snag test a small steel ball is moved to and fro across the specimen under a constant load. It is in effect a particular type of abrasion test and the number of passes required to break through the specimen is a measure of the abrasion resistance. The effect of a few passes is to produce a series of ridges at right angles to the direction of traverse (see Fig. 3.21). The action of the ball (under normal load) traversing across the specimen is thought to be as follows. The normal load depresses the ball into the surface, thus creating a ridge around the ball. As the ball begins to move, the poromeric surface in contact with the ball is held by frictional forces. This produces tensile forces in the surface at the rear of the ball and creates a high ridge in front of the ball. In the ridge area there will be complex forces acting in both compression and extension.

In the limiting case the tensile forces overcome the frictional forces and the ball will slip over the hump, compressing it in passing, and the process recommences. The compressed ridges do not fully recover and the surface finish and its adhesion to the microporous surface layer are presumably weakened (see Fig. 3.22). Subsequent passes produce more weakening until rupture at the base edge of the ridge is finally produced and the ball then begins to abrade the microporous surface layer (see Fig. 3.23). Once the surface finish is broken most poromeric materials do not have the sort of microporous surface region which is abrasion resistant and the material is relatively quickly abraded.

It would appear that friction is of major importance in the snag test abrasion rating but, of course, to reduce the friction of the surface finish could be in conflict with other properties such as flexibility. The snag test is only one aspect of the overall abrasion mechanism and, for example, impact cutting would be influenced by other properties.

STITCHING AND BEADED EDGE

We have briefly examined the surfaces of some poromeric materials when stitched at a beaded edge. It was noticeable that the stitches penetrated some poromerics more deeply than others (Fig. 3.24). In some cases the surface layer was damaged by the needle and some of the underlying microporous material was brought to the surface.

The beaded edge is in fact the opposite situation to surface 'break' with the surface layer under considerable tension. These areas were carefully examined to see if the tensile forces had produced any incipient flaws in the surface material, but none were found.

It has only been possible to indicate how the Stereoscan could be used to study more closely a number of shoe-forming operations. The behaviour on lasting, the orange peel effect, folding, wrinkling, thermosetting and embossing are all obvious contenders for study by this technique.

SUMMARY

The Stereoscan has been used to clearly illustrate the structure of poromeric materials. Different types of microporous structures and the different arrangements of binder in the base felt region have been examined and classified. It has also been possible to show the detailed behaviour of the fold in surface 'break' and how this is influenced by the structure. The abrasion process involved in a standard test has also been studied.

ACKNOWLEDGEMENTS

Our thanks are due to the Directors of the Dunlop Company for permission to publish this paper and to Mrs C. Smewin, Mr M. Higgs and Mr M. Walters for their invaluable help.

CHAPTER 4

Foot comfort and foot hygiene

A. G. C. HUYSMANS

INTRODUCTION

THE WORD comfort is sometimes veiled in a kind of mystery.
At times it is preferably disregarded for economic reasons, and especially
in comparisons of synthetic materials with leather it is often used to
bring out the superior properties of the natural product at the expense
of the synthetic materials.

With the advent of the poromerics a type of material has entered the
market which in terms of comfort is an important milestone on the way
towards the ideal 'leather'. Thus, comfort is a concept that has attracted
considerable interest, but it has appeared that the absence of a clear
definition often leads to confusion and misunderstanding.

Starting from the functions of foot and shoe we will try to come to a
clear definition of comfort. Apart from this, we have selected from the
many aspects of this subject a few specific items for a more detailed
discussion. These aspects have been studied in our laboratories to weigh
up the merits of some poromerics against leather.

DEFINITION OF COMFORT

If we want to define the concept comfort, we should have a clear notion
of the functions of the shoe as well as of the demands made by a proper
functioning of the foot. As far as the shoe is concerned it has become
clear from talks with medical men and shoe experts that the main
function of the shoe is to protect. In this respect we distinguish
between:

1 protection from mechanical influences
2 protection from temperature influences
3 protection from moisture influences.

In all three instances we have to deal with influences from outside.
The functions of the foot could be described as follows:

1 The foot carries the weight of the body
2 The foot forms part of the body mechanism of locomotion
3 Together with the hand, the foot forms that part of the body
surface where the temperature of the body is controlled in the
first instance.

For a proper functioning of the foot it is necessary that the protective material does not impede these functions of the foot. Defining the concept comfort it could therefore be said that:

'Comfort is the degree in which the protective task of the shoe is adapted to the demands made by a normal functioning of the foot.'

THE FIELDS DETERMINING COMFORT

The functions of the shoe as well as the demands made by a normal functioning of the foot cover two widely divergent fields, viz.

1 The field where the mechanical behaviour plays an important role
2 The field dealing with the physical behaviour.

It may be well to point out here that good comfort makes demands in both areas, so that there can only be a question of good comfort if the mechanical, as well as the physical, demands are fulfilled. However, this does not imply that the two areas are to be regarded as equivalent.

If we look more closely at the demands made on the shoe, we come to the following specifications:

MECHANICAL REQUIREMENTS

1 The shoe must offer protective cover to the foot
2 The shoe should mould itself to the specific shape of the wearer's foot
3 The shoe will have to adapt itself to dimensional changes of the foot
4 The shoe must be flexible, permitting it to follow the movements of the foot
5 Deformations imposed by the foot should not lead to pressure at the joint
6 The shoe should not grow so large in wear that the foot starts shifting.

For the poromeric materials which initially presented difficulties in the adaption to the shape of the foot a more specified fitting range has been suggested, but the shoe industry has not reacted enthusiastically to this idea.

In what directions have the makers of poromeric materials tried to find a solution? We found two trends:

1 The use of low-modulus material
2 The use of hydrophilic materials in the substrate, which introduces special properties, making the material approach leather in this respect.

By its low stress-strain ratio the low-modulus material will readily adapt itself to the shape of the individual foot and also easily follow the dimensional changes of the foot during the day. After the shoe has been taken off, it returns to the original shape, and hence does not show any permanent deformations.

The second trend, namely, the use of hydrophilic materials in the

49

substrate, is of considerable interest, because it offers the possibility of incorporating the desired properties in a way similar to that applied to leather.

In this case the adaptation to the shape of the foot will take place by deformation in originally tight places where the exudate is directly given off to the upper. As the material takes up the moisture, it will deform more easily and yield to the pressure exerted. Also, this hydrophilic material will expand as it takes up moisture, so that it will be able to follow the dimensional changes of the foot during the day.

At this point it may be interesting to say something about the possibility of measuring this property. A known method is the determination of the change in length of a strip of material when this is transferred from an atmosphere of, say, 20°C and 50% RH to 32°C and 95% RH (comparable with foot conditions). However, the values obtained are of little significance, because too little is known about the changes occurring at the foot. It is believed that a value of greater significance is obtained with the SATRA Dome Plasticity apparatus generally known from the measurement of the percentage 'set'. After determining the percentage set, the clamped material is transferred to a space of 32°C, 95% RH and then back to 20°C, 50% RH. After equilibrium has been reached, the percentage set is calculated from the height of the dome, under both circumstances. We then get the following information:

(a) An impression of the percentage set which is closer to reality
(b) An impression of the sensitivity to moisture, but now expressed as a difference in percentage set. It is preferable to express it in this way rather than as a change in length of a strip of material.

Table 4.1. Sensitivity to temperature and moisture of four shoe upper materials

| Material code | Fibre type | % Set | | | Sensitivity to temp. and moisture (2)-(3) |
		After moist heat setting (1)	32°C 95% RH (2)	20°C 50% RH (3)	
A	Hydrophobic	47	37½	36½	1
B	Slightly hydrophilic	53	45	27	18
C	Strongly hydrophilic	96	80	50	30
D	Leather	83	79	67	12

Some of the results obtained are summarized in Table 4.1. The materials can be described as follows:

A is a poromeric material based on hydrophobic fibre web
B is a poromeric material based on slightly hydrophilic fibre web
C is a poromeric material based on strongly hydrophilic fibre web
D is leather.

In these materials there occur not only differences in type of fibre, but also differences in density, different ratios of fibre to bonding agent, etc. Without going into details it can be said that this method gives a fair picture of what may be expected from different materials.

Reverting to the poromeric material based on a hydrophilic fibre web we find that it also comes up to other requirements. As the hydrophilic material takes up moisture, the resulting reduction of the stress-strain ratio will make the material appreciably more supple at the moment when it has to meet the highest demands and in places where this is needed most. Also, the greater flexibility will reduce the discomfort at pressure points.

Generally, the mechanical properties we have just discussed are felt to have a greater effect on comfort than the physical properties to be discussed next.

PHYSICAL REQUIREMENTS

Before we set out to discuss the physical aspects, let us consider what happens in and around the foot. The body uses the foot preferentially for regulating the temperature. For this purpose the foot secretes a diluted salt solution through sweat glands. Given an ideal operation, the heat needed to evaporate the moisture will be extracted from the body In addition to the secretion of moisture by the sweat glands there occurs a less important separation of moisture as vapour, the *perspiratio insensibilis,* resulting from the foot's own metabolism. Depending on the activity of the body, more or less heat will have to be carried off, implying that a varying amount of moisture has to be evaporated.

The moisture, heat and salts which are then present simultaneously, not only exert their influence on comfort, but are also decisive on foot hygiene.

First, we will examine the discharge of sweat. According to Mitton and Grimwade *(J. Soc. Leather Trade Chem.,* **43**, 192, 1959) in an article by Gran the amount of moisture secreted by the foot ranges from *c.* 3 g/h at rest to 15–20 g/h for strenuous activities or heavy marches.

The shoe must now fulfil the requirements of forming no impediment to this strongly fluctuating flow of moisture. What happens if the shoe does impede the flow of moisture? If moisture is carried off inadequately or if there is no discharge at all, the sweat will cover a greater or smaller part of the skin, cause the sweat glands to close down and hamper the temperature regulation, which results in a less comfortable feeling. The criteria handled to judge comfort in this sense have been found to be the following:

1 The total amount of moisture that can be carried off from a shod foot compared with the amount of moisture that would have been given off by an unshod foot under equal circumstances

2 The part of the foot surface that is covered with sweat

3 The moisture content of the hose after wearing (for standardized hose and material).

Although these aspects would seem to be different, they are in reality closely bound up, for if the shoe is unable to discharge the amount of moisture from which the unshod foot would be willing to part, the secreted moisture can no longer evaporate and will persist as liquid on part of the skin surface. It is clear that also the hose will then become wet.

For judging a property, it is usually desirable to have a criterion which is not only unambiguous, but also permits measuring. In the case of wear trials the measurement of the moisture content of the hose is best suited. At the laboratory, use may be made of the PA test developed by SATRA. This test has not been designed for the shoe as such, but for judging the upper material, on which it can provide extensive information. It will be known that in the PA test a combination of upper material and hose (with or without lining) separates two spaces. In one space (hose side) the atmosphere is maintained at 32°C and 100% RH, in the other (upper material side) the conditions are maintained at 20°C and 65% RH. In the latter space the air is kept in motion with a fan. The measurements concern the amount of water vapour passed through and the amount of moisture taken up by the upper material and the hose (and the lining, if present). The measurements are repeated at certain intervals, so that an impression is also obtained of the rates of permeability and absorption.

For a proper assessment of the results it is well to realize the merits and shortcomings of this method. Drawbacks are the following:

(a) The test evaluates a material combination which occurs only in part of the shoe

(b) The test simulates the ideal condition in the shoe, assuming only vapour contact between foot and hose

(c) In the test the total production of moisture is limited by the materials to be tested, whereas in the shoe the foot determines the amount of moisture to be carried off

(d) Measuring in this test takes place in a region where formation of condensate is possible or likely. An accurate and reproducible adjustment of the temperature gradient over the material under test is therefore of the greatest importance.

Despite these restrictions and idealization this test is a valuable tool in comparing materials for the following reasons:

1 Differences in moisture content of the hose material give an impression of the direction in which differences in comfort are to be expected

2 The total amount of water vapour discharged from the jar can be determined more accurately than the moisture content of the hose material by summing up the measured increase in weight of hose and upper and the measured permeability. Our measurements show that there is a good correlation between these values, as appears from Fig. 4.1. (Although it is not exactly known how much moisture the foot will give off under certain conditions, a higher value of the total discharge may be expected to imply greater comfort.)

3 The test gives an impression of the ratio between the amounts of moisture passed through and absorbed

4 The presence or absence of moisture in the clamped edge gives information about the possibility of moisture transport in the plane of the material.

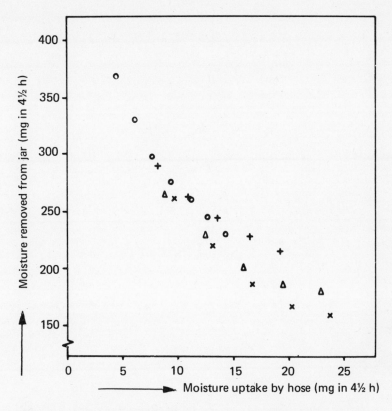

Fig. 4.1. *Moisture removed from jar versus moisture uptake on four substrates combined with different coating layers in PA Test.*

In our investigation we were specially interested in the relative importance of absorption and permeability. Also, we were anxious to know if there was a correlation between these quantities. We had the opportunity to combine substrates of different absorption capacities with coating layers of different permeabilities. These combinations were subjected to the PA test. The results are summarized in Figs 4.2 to 4.5.

The permeability axis represents the amount of moisture passed through the test area in 4½ hours. Also the absorption values have been determined after 4½ hours of PA test. Figs 4.2 and 4.3 show a decrease of the moisture content of the hose as well as in the upper material at increasing permeability. It might even be inferred that at a high permeability, comparable with that of good quality calf leather, the nature of the substrate does not play a role any more.

A similar picture is presented by Fig. 4.4, where the dotted line represents the situation where no absorption takes place at all, so that all of the water vapour carried off is due to the permeability. This case is also a clear illustration of the fact that as the permeability is reduced the absorption becomes more important, in many instances even more so than the permeability. (See also Supplement to Fig. 4.4 at the end of this chapter.) Also in Fig. 4.5, giving the relation between the

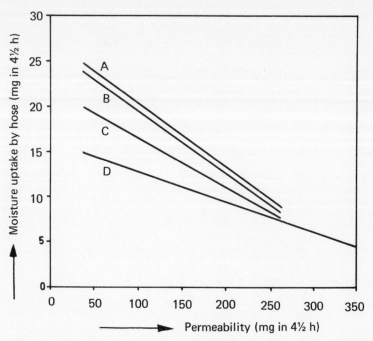

Fig. 4.2. Moisture uptake versus permeability on four substrates combined with different coating layers in PA Test.

moisture content of the hose material and that of the upper, we see a preference for the hydrophilic materials.

In a discussion with Mr J. G. Butlin, of SATRA, he suggested a more conspicuous representation of the results. This has been done in Figs 4.6 and 4.7 where the points of equal moisture content of the hose (Fig. 4.6) and those of equal total discharge (Fig. 4.7), on the axes for the hydrophilic properties and the permeability, have been interconnected.

On the hydrophilic axis we have plotted the moisture uptake of the material at 20°C and 95% RH, expressed as a percentage of the moisture uptake of leather under the same circumstances. It will be clear that the area in the right-hand top corner of the graphs represents good comfort, while that at the bottom left represents poor comfort. The trend of the corresponding values shows that the moisture uptake of the hose as well as the total amount of moisture carried off are criteria for the evaluation of comfort. It is recommendable to test some materials from these fields for practical comfort by means of wear trials. It should be expressly stated here that no flowing curves may be expected with this set-up, because not only was the fibre type different, but also—simultaneously —the density of the material, the amount of filler, the structure of the substrates, etc.

The foregoing relates exclusively to the results of the PA test.

Now for the situation in the shoe. In Gran's publication from which we quoted earlier we find the following subdivision of the amount carried off:

10% due to permeability
50% due to absorption (25% by upper material)
                       (25% by the shoe bottom)
40% due to pumping action during walking.

It need cause no surprise that the permeability has such a modest share in the total discharge. On the one hand a considerable part of the permeating area has been rendered inactive by the use of auxiliaries such as counter and toe puff, on the other hand the resistance to the permeability has been considerably increased by the use of adhesive and the presence of double layers of material at the place where the tongue is fitted. It may therefore be asked if the method of manufacturing the shoe could not be improved in regard to the choice of the materials for the auxiliaries; so that the good properties of leather and poromerics, which are potentially present, would be used more profitably.

It is understandable that leather experts assign the differences in comfort between leather and poromerics, apart from differences in mechanical properties, to differences in absorption capacity. In this respect we therefore expect a great deal from materials based on hydrophilic fibre webs.

Will it be possible to replace the permeability in the shoe by a higher

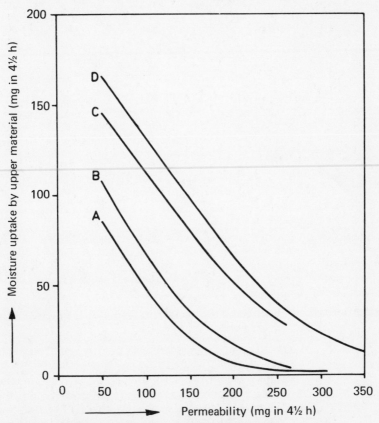

Fig. 4.3. Moisture uptake versus permeability on four substrates combined with different coating layers in PA Test.

absorption capacity? This question can only be answered in the affirmative if the rate of moisture desorption in the periods when the shoe is not worn is such that there is no question of accumulation of moisture. If the rate of desorption in these periods is too low, this will result in a lower absorption capacity in subsequent wear periods, which will manifest itself in decreasing comfort.

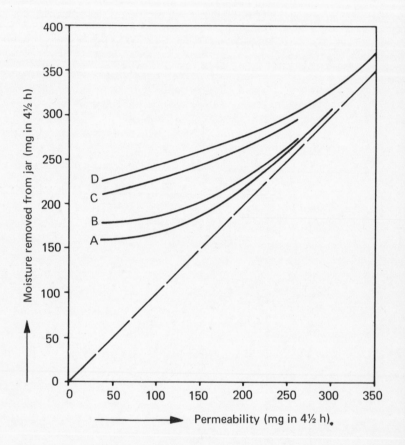

Fig. 4.4. Moisture removed from jar versus permeability on four substrates combined with different coating layers in PA Test.

As the second point in the field of the physical requirements we mention the temperature influence. As yet, little is known about the heat insulation, and it is generally assumed that it is of minor importance. It is known that moisture has a detrimental effect on the thermal insulation. As the shoe separates two spaces of 32°C and 100% RH, and of 20°C and 65% RH, respectively, the thermal insulation may play an important role in the moisture balance if there is condensate formation. It is, therefore, recommendable to study this field more accurately.

Finally, let us take a look at the foot salts. In the case of leather not only the foot salts but also the salt content of the sole forms a major contribution to the spue phenomenon. When the material becomes moist, these salts migrate into the upper leather and settle on the outside as the moisture evaporates.

The poromeric materials themselves contain hardly any salts. When the shoe has synthetic soles the foot salts are the only solids that can come into contact with the upper material.

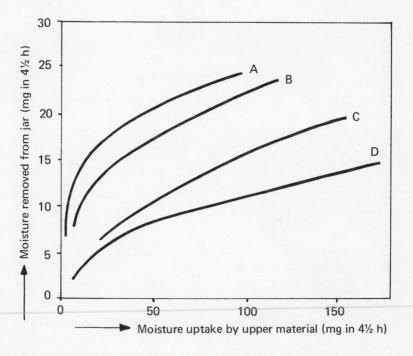

Fig. 4.5. Moisture uptake by hose versus moisture uptake by four substrates combined with different coating layers in PA Test.

What exactly happens in the combination foot-hose-upper material? On the naked foot the foot salts after evaporation of the moisture will crystallize on the foot itself, and will be removed by washing. When the foot is surrounded by a hose and a shoe, the exudate will usually be taken up by the hose. Two things may then happen:
   (a) The hose passes the exudate on to the upper material, where it gives rise to spue on the outside
   (b) The moisture taken up by the hose evaporates, the vapour is carried off via the upper material (absorption and permeability), the salts remain in the hose and are removed by washing the hose.
The transport of moisture from the hose to the upper material via the

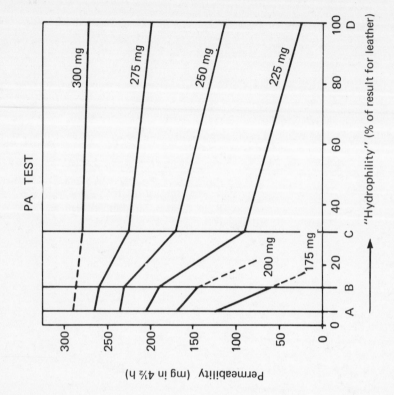

Fig. 4.7. Permeability versus hydrophility (the quantities given on the figure show total moisture removed from jar in 4½ hours).

Fig. 4.6. Permeability versus hydrophility (the quantities given on the figure show moisture uptake by hose in 4½ hours).

vapour phase will be promoted by a low RH in the space between hose and shoe (high permeability, high absorption capacity, effective pumping action).

In conclusion it should be remarked that, while the poromerics are generally credited with the property 'easy clean, easy care', this characteristic is strictly limited to the upper material. The poromerics will make even more demands on foot hygiene and the washing of socks than leather.

SUPPLEMENT TO FIG. 4.4

As mentioned earlier, the total amount of moisture discharged from the PA test jar is strongly influenced by the material under test, whereas in the shoe the foot determines how much moisture has to be carried off.

If moisture is only carried off in the vapour phase, the maximum uptake is determined by the equilibrium situations at 20°C, 65% RH and 32°C, 100% RH. This maximum amount is independent of the permeability and can be represented in Fig. 4.4 by a line parallel to the dashed line. For clearness this has been done separately for the materials A to D in Figs 4.8–4.11. In each figure the dashed line *a* represents the theoretical case where all the vapour carried off is due to permeability. Line b represents the amount of moisture carried off by the combined effects of permeability and maximum absorption. Line c gives the results of measurements with the PA test and is taken from Fig. 4.4.

We compared the materials at a 100 mg permeability level and found the following picture:

Material A: PQ represents the amount of moisture carried off by permeability. QR represents the maximum amount of moisture the material is able to absorb from the vapour phase at 32°C, 100% RH. From the total amount absorbed QS, part RS is present in the liquid state. In the hatched area we find liquid water in the porous structure (Fig. 4.8).

Material B: Here the situation is comparable with material A. However, the hatched area is smaller (Fig. 4.9).

Material C: At the 100 mg permeability level we find QS as the amount absorbed, and QR as the maximum amount that can be absorbed by this material at 32°C, 100% RH. RS could be regarded as an over-capacity. No liquid water is present, perhaps even at zero permeability (Fig. 4.10).

Material D: The situation is comparable with that for material C. Compared with material C we find a more important over-capacity in absorption (Fig. 4.11).

Again it should be pointed out that the foregoing holds for the situation in the PA test. In a subsequent investigation we will try to indicate the areas of practical interest in the figures mentioned. We will have to take into account the effective permeating and absorbing surface area of the upper material. Besides, it will have to be investigated by means of wear trials whether SATRA's finding that the 4½ hour PA test is comparable with a normal wearing period and is sufficiently accurate.

59

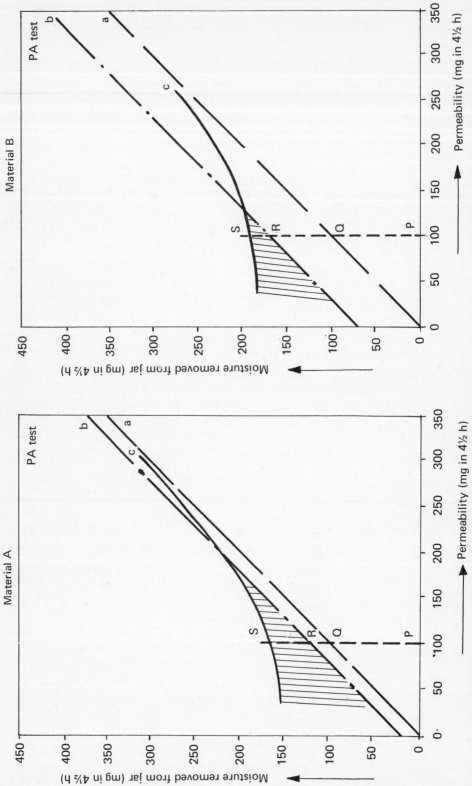

Fig. 4.9 Moisture removed from jar versus permeability

Fig. 4.8 Moisture removed from jar versus permeability

60

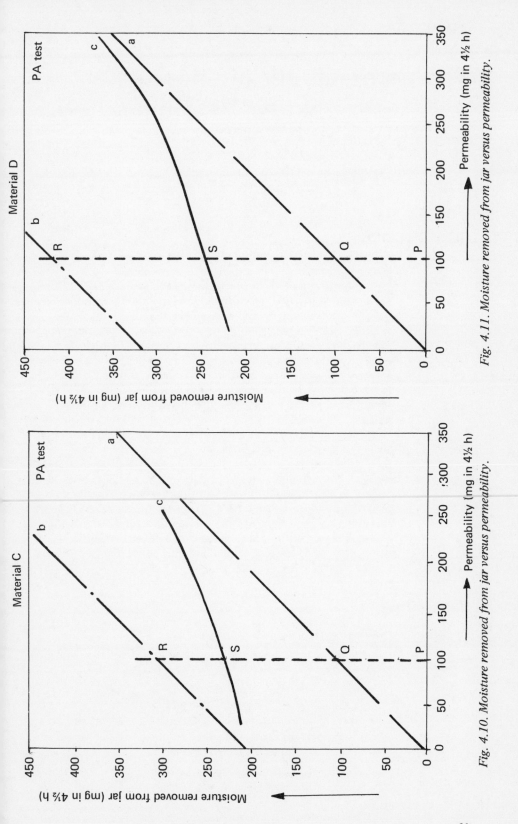

Fig. 4.11. Moisture removed from jar versus permeability.

Fig. 4.10. Moisture removed from jar versus permeability.

61

CHAPTER **5**

The permeability of shoe upper materials and its effect upon foot comfort and hygiene

K. R. BUSER, I. C. CHU and P. J. GRAHAM*

INTRODUCTION

WATER vapour permeability is an essential property of shoe upper materials, be they natural or man-made. Permeable shoe upper materials allow moisture inside shoes to pass through to the outside and thereby provide the relatively dry conditions necessary for foot comfort. Though our basic studies on foot comfort confirm that some other factors such as internal shoe pressure and the area expansion, modulus, and moisture absorbability of shoe upper materials may also contribute to foot comfort, water vapour permeability remains the single most important property essential to foot comfort. Extensive wear tests [1] clearly indicate that the comfort level during wear is directly related to the water vapour permeability of the shoe upper material. The importance of water vapour permeability to comfort makes it vital that we understand how water vapour passes through poromeric materials and what means are at our disposal for its control.

In complex structures like poromeric materials, water vapour can permeate through solid polymer regions and through open pores therein. The mechanism of vapour transport through a simple structure, i.e. a solid film without pores, has been extensively studied [2, 3, 4] and reviewed in textbooks [5, 6]. The essential elements of permeation processes important to shoe upper materials are reviewed briefly here before proceeding to our studies of poromeric shoe upper materials.

PERMEATION

PERMEATION PROCESS THROUGH A SOLID FILM

Permeation of water vapour through a solid film takes place in three steps:

1 Water adsorption on one side
2 Dissolved water migration through film
3 Water desorption from other side.

The driving force for these events (Fig. 5.1) is the difference in water concentration on opposite sides of the film.

* Contribution from the Fabrics & Finishes Dept., Experimental Station Laboratory, E. I. du Pont de Nemours & Co., Wilmington, Delaware.

A mathematical expression for the water vapour permeation rate through a nonporous film as derived from Fick's first law of diffusion and Henry's law [5, 6] relating to pressures of gases above liquids follows:

$$\text{Permeation rate} = DS\left(\frac{\Delta p}{\Delta x}\right)$$

This equation states that the permeation rate through a solid film is equal to the product of diffusion coefficient (D), the solubility coefficient (S) and the partial pressure gradient ($\Delta p/\Delta x$) of water vapour through a film of thickness (Δx). For a particular film-permeant pair, constants S and D can be replaced with p which is now the permeability constant characteristic of the film-permeant pair.

DRY SIDE

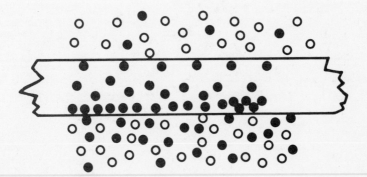

WET SIDE

$$\text{PERMEATION RATE} = DS\left(\frac{\Delta p}{\Delta x}\right)$$

Fig. 5.1. Permeation of water vapour through solid film.

Both of these coefficients (S and D) can be determined by a sorption-desorption experiment performed in one apparatus (Fig. 5.2). The solubility coefficient (S) can be determined from the equilibrium weight gain of the film when exposed to constant water vapour pressure [6]. The diffusion coefficient (D) can be determined by measuring the rate of weight loss in the desorption cycle of the same experiment.

PERMEATION PROCESS THROUGH A POROUS FILM

Permeation of water vapour through porous material is much more complex (and less well defined) than it is through solid film. This is

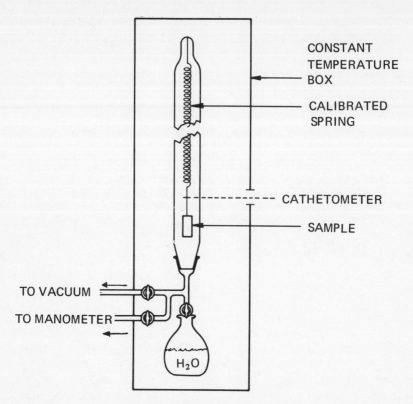

Fig. 5.2. Sorption–Desorption apparatus.

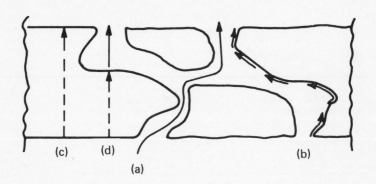

(a) Permeation in the open pore space

(b) Permeation along the side of the wall

(c) Permeation through the bulk of the solid material

(d) Some combinations of (a), (b), and (c)

Fig. 5.3. Permeation of water vapour through a porous material.

because porous materials are more heterogeneous, have internal structures difficult to describe accurately but which offer additional transport mechanisms for water vapour permeation.

Fig. 5.3 shows a schematic diagram of permeation of water vapour through a porous material. The permeation process may take place in (a) the open pore space, (b) along the side of the wall, (c) through the bulk of the material, and (d) possibly some combination of these. If the porous material is quite thick as in the case of shoe upper material, the contribution of mechanism (c) can reasonably be assumed to be negligible (for reasons that will be apparent later).

The permeation rate of water vapour through a pore depends on:

1 The average size of the pores
2 The length of the path through which water vapour must travel
3 The speed of water molecules (temperature dependent)
4 The frequency of collision with air molecules (pressure and molecule size dependent).

The first two factors are related to the *structure* of the porous material; the last two factors are related to the *environmental conditions.*

Permeation of water vapour through a pore by surface diffusion requires the molecules to migrate along the internal surface of the pores rather than in the void space of the pores. Migration takes place as a result of the concentration gradient along the surface. For a condensible vapour, surface diffusion in the pore may take place independently and simultaneously with gas diffusion. The rate of surface diffusion is dependent upon the internal surface area of the material, but independent of the nature of the permeant gas with which the pore space is filled.

Table 5.1. Water vapour permeability of poromerics and leathers

	PV ($mg/cm^2/hr$)	
	Unfinished	Finished
Poromeric Material	4-6	1-2
Leathers	5-7	1-3

Table 5.1 gives the range of water vapour permeabilities* for Corfam poromeric materials and leathers before and after the application of an acrylic finish coat. Unfinished Corfam has a permeability approximately the same as unfinished leathers. Finish coats reduce the water vapour permeability of Corfam poromeric material more than leather. To understand and respond to this, it is necessary that we know the relative importance and contributions of various permeation mechanisms to overall water vapour permeability.

* *Water Vapour Permeability:* In these studies permeability values (PV) were measured at 24·4°C and 90% RH (against 0% RH) and expressed as $g/100 \ m^2/hr$. SATRA permeability values are measured at 20°C and 65% RH and expressed as $mg/cm^2/hr$. Conversion factor: SATRA PV $\times$ 1·81 $\times$ 10^3 = our PV. All graphs show both unit scales.

PERMEATION THROUGH CORFAM POROMERIC MATERIAL (FIG. 5.4)

Unfinished Corfam poromeric material is an impregnated web having macropores as well as micropores. The impregnated web is open enough to permit flow of liquid water and free transport of water vapour. The microporous layer contains millions of micropores per square inch, so fine $(1-3\mu)$ that they repel liquid water, but the layer shows a vapour permeability by itself of about 7·2 PV units. The large number of fine pores in this layer means there is a relatively high internal surface area.

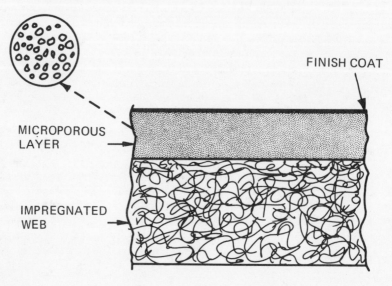

Fig. 5.4. Structure of a poromeric material.

In view of the different permeation mechanisms operating in a composite structure, we can expect different contributions to PV by the macropores and by the micropores. Referring to Fig. 5.3, permeation by gas diffusion (Path a) is a possibility for all gases like air, CO_2, H_2, and water vapour, but permeation by surface diffusion (Path b) can also occur with readily condensible gases like water vapour. Thus, it is possible that the observed permeation rate for water is the combined result of 'gas diffusion' inside of the pore space and 'surface diffusion' along internal surfaces. We can determine whether this is so by comparing actual versus calculated diffusion rates.

The permeation rate of a gas A through a porous material (containing gas B in pores) under a given partial pressure gradient is proportional to the diffusion coefficient (D_{A-B}). If carbon dioxide is the permeant gas and we know its diffusion coefficient (against nitrogen), we can calculate the permeation rate of water vapour through the same structure by the equation:

$$R_{(H_2O)} = \frac{D_{(H_2O-N_2)}}{D_{(CO_2-N_2)}} \times R_{CO_2}$$

This assumes water behaves like a permanent gas and is noncondensible in poromeric material (that is, surface diffusion is negligible). However, if 'surface diffusion' is taking place simultaneously, the calculated permeation rate based on the pure 'gas diffusion' model would be less than the experimental value. The difference between the calculated and the experimental permeation rates is attributed to 'surface diffusion.'

We measured the permeation of carbon dioxide and water vapour through unfinished Corfam in a nitrogen atmosphere (Table 5.2). By gas diffusion alone, water vapour is expected to permeate through Corfam faster than CO_2 by a factor of 1·64. The experimentally observed values showed that water vapour permeates 1·92 times faster than carbon dioxide. This is more than can be accounted for by experimental error. Therefore, about 90% of the water vapour coming through the unfinished Corfam poromeric material must be the result of 'gas diffusion' and 10% the result of 'surface diffusion'

Table 5.2. Permeation of carbon dioxide and water vapour through unfinished poromeric material

	Permeation rate, mol/100 m^2/h		Diffusion mechanism	
Gas pair	Calculated	Observed	Gas	Surface
CO_2 N_2	—	264 ± 13	264	0
H_2O N_2	432	506 ± 25	432	74 (13%)

When these experiments were repeated in a hydrogen atmosphere, we observed a substantial increase in the vapour permeation rate (as expected) through the hydrogen atmosphere. Within experimental error, however, the amount of water vapour coming through unfinished Corfam by 'surface diffusion' mechanism was approximately the same in nitrogen and hydrogen atmosphere.

We conclude from these results that water vapour permeation through unfinished Corfam takes place predominantly in the pore space by a gas diffusion mechanism with a small ($\sim$10%) contribution due to 'surface diffusion'.

WATER VAPOUR PERMEABILITY OF FINISHED POROMERIC MATERIALS

The effect of finishing on permeability is demonstrated by spraying an acrylic finish coat on to unfinished Corfam substrate which has an initial water vapour permeability of 4·4 (mg/cm^2/hr). In Fig. 5.5 water vapour permeability plotted against the amount of applied finish coat (oz/yd^2) shows a sharp drop between 0·1 and 0·2 oz/yd^2. This suggests a change in the mode of water vapour permeation. We had shown earlier that for the unfinished poromerics, 'gas diffusion' is the controlling transport mechanism. The data shown in Fig. 5.5 indicates that after application of 0·2 oz/yd^2 of finish coat, 'gas diffusion' is no longer the controlling mechanism. We believe that the break in this curve marks the

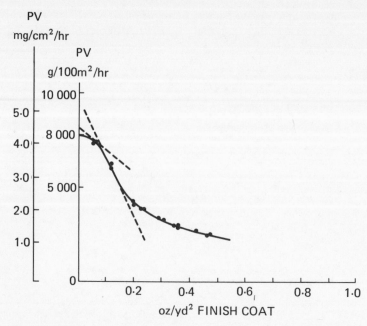

Fig. 5.5. Water vapour permeability of Corfam as a function of the amount of finish coat applied.

point where the open pores on the surface of the unfinished material are mostly covered by a continuous film of finish. Water vapour molecules, having travelled through the substrate by way of gas diffusion, must now diffuse through a solid film in order to complete the permeation process.

Complete coverage by the finish coat can easily be determined by measuring whether or not gas can flow through the material under a *small* pressure difference ($\sim$ 3 mm Hg). We measured the gas flow as a function of the amount of finish coat applied. Table 5.3 shows that the gas (N_2) flow was reduced by a factor of about 8 000 when 0·2 oz/yd^2 of finish coat was applied to unfinished Corfam poromeric substrate.

Table 5.3. Gas flow rate through finished and unfinished poromerics

Amount of finish applied oz/yd^2	Gas (N_2) flow rate* (cc/cm^2/min/Δp mm Hg) $\times$ 10^3
0	800·0
0·07	40·0
0·14	0·9
0·21	0·1

* Gas flow rate is measured under a pressure difference Δp = 3 mm Hg

Complete surface coverage by the finish coat seems to depend on surface topography and pore size. Fig. 5.6 shows the water vapour permeability of a calfskin leather as a function of the amount of finish coat applied. This calfskin leather specimen has a natural grain pattern (i.e. a rough surface) and an average pore size of about 50μ; this is believed to be the reason why a continuous film of the finish coat was not formed on the calfskin substrate until about 0.5 oz/yd^2 was applied (about 0.75 mil*). At this point, water vapour permeability drops sharply as noted in the plot of 'water vapour permeability' versus 'finish coat'. Up to a finish thickness of about 0.5 oz/yd^2, permeation takes place predominantly by 'gas diffusion'; after this point, permeation of water vapour must be completed by diffusing through a continuous film. We have found that this transition point can be further delayed towards thicker finish coatings by controlling pore size (at the surface) and surface topography of unfinished substrate.

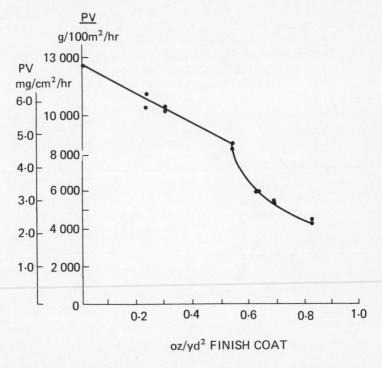

Fig. 5.6. Water vapour permeability of calfskin as a function of the amount of finish coat.

HOW WATER VAPOUR PERMEABILITY OF THE WHOLE STRUCTURE RELATES TO ITS COMPONENT LAYERS

The total permeability of a structure can be calculated with an impedance equation [5] if the permeability values of its component layers are known. For example, if an unsupported finish coat (0.5 mil thick, permeability value, 3.0) is combined with an unfinished Corfam substrate (permeability value, 4.4), the water vapour permeability of the

* In this chapter 'mil' = thousandth of an inch

composite of these two layers is calculated to be 1·8 by the following equations:

$$\frac{1}{(PV)} = \frac{1}{(PV)_a} + \frac{1}{(PV)_b}$$

$$\frac{1}{1·8} = \frac{1}{4·4} + \frac{1}{3·0}$$

The measured PV value for the same composite was 1·9.

Using this impedance equation, we computed the water vapour permeabilities of entire poromeric structures as a function of the thickness of the applied finish coat and compared them with the observed values. The results in Fig. 5.7 show good agreement between calculated and observed water vapour permeabilities in the region where more than 0·2 oz/yd^2 of finish coat is applied. The observed values in regions where the finish coat is thinner than 0·2 oz/yd^2 are higher than calculated because the finish coat is discontinuous and the impedance equation assumes a continuous film of finish.

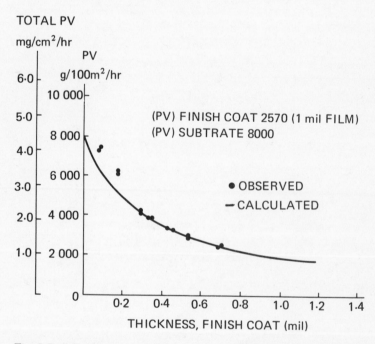

Fig. 5.7. Calculated and measure WVP of Corfam vs. amount of finish coat.

There are times when a reasonably thick finish coat (0·6–1·0 mil) is needed to provide hiding or to control aesthetics for a poromeric material. In these cases it can be more important to increase the vapour permeability of the finish rather than the PV of the other component

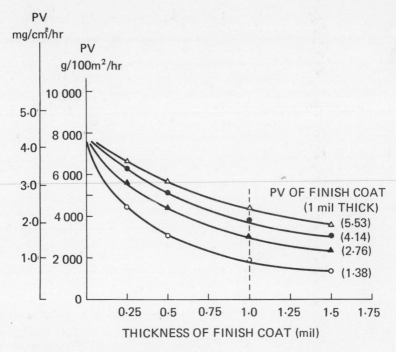

Fig. 5.8. Calculated WVP of finished Corfam with finish coats of varying water vapour permeabilities.

parts. Fig. 5.8 shows the effect on permability of a basic Corfam structure of 4·4 PV when it is finished in varying thickness with finish coats of different basic permeabilities. Varying the water vapour permeability of the finish coat from 1·4 to 5·5 changes the PV of the total structure from 1·1 to 2·5 PV.

Table 5.4. WVP of free polymer films (1 mil thick)

	PV–mg/cm²/hr. (approx for 1 mil)
Polyethylene (high density)	0·0017
Polyvinyl chloride	0·021–0·033
Polyacrylonitrile	0·17
Polyvinylbutyral	0·41
Nylon 66	0·47
Standard acrylic finish coat	1·7
Polyvinyl alcohol	1·8
Cellulose acetate	3·2
Polyurethane (high % soft segments)	4·2
Polytetramethylene ether glycol (2 000 mw)	4·4
	PV (15 mil)
Microporous film (used in Corfam)	7·2

The water vapour permeabilities of common polymer films (1 mil thick) are listed in Table 5.4. Some of these values were taken from the published literature and converted to PV units (mg/cm²/hr from 65% RH to 0% RH) and some were measured in our own laboratory. Cellulose derivatives, polyvinyl alcohol, and polytetramethylene ether glycol have the highest permeability to water vapour. Polyurethanes with sufficiently high content of soft polymer segment are also very permeable to water vapour. With these highly permeable polymers as binders in the finish coat, a water vapour permeability of about 2·5 can be achieved without changing the structure of the substrate.

It is worth noting that the water vapour permeability of the most permeable continuous film is still not comparable to that of a microporous film. A 15 mil microporous film can have a PV of about 7·2—a value probably unattainable by a solid film of equivalent thickness.

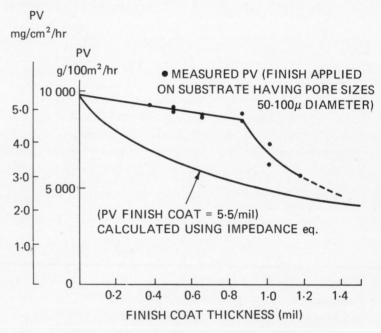

Fig. 5.9. Effect of finishes on large pores of poromeric material.

The importance of micro-discontinuities in maintaining a high water vapour permeability in finish coated poromeric materials is further supported by the experimental results in Fig. 5.9. When a substrate having an average pore size of 50-100 microns diameter was finish coated lightly, the pores were incompletely covered. The measured PV was higher than calculated as shown by the points in Fig. 5.9. If a continuous film of the highest possible water permeability (i.e. 5·5 unit/mil) had been used on the same substrate, the calculated PV of the composite structure would have been represented by the lower curve. Although the two lines tend to approach each other at more complete surface coverage, the difference in PV is quite significant at film thickness less than 0·8 mil (0·55 oz/yd²).

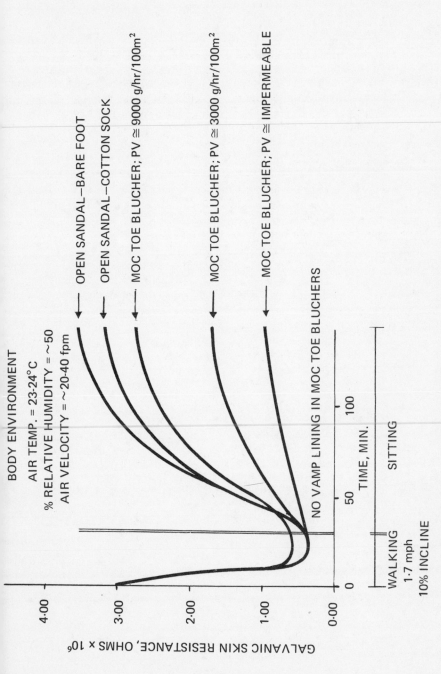

BODY ENVIRONMENT
AIR TEMP. = 23-24°C
% RELATIVE HUMIDITY = ~50
AIR VELOCITY = ~20-40 fpm

← OPEN SANDAL–BARE FOOT
← OPEN SANDAL–COTTON SOCK
← MOC TOE BLUCHER; PV ≅ 9000 g/hr/100m²
← MOC TOE BLUCHER; PV ≅ 3000 g/hr/100m²
← MOC TOE BLUCHER; PV ≅ IMPERMEABLE

NO VAMP LINING IN MOC TOE BLUCHERS

WALKING
1·7 mph
10% INCLINE

SITTING

TIME, MIN.

0   50   100

GALVANIC SKIN RESISTANCE, OHMS × 10⁶

0·00   1·00   2·00   3·00   4·00

Fig. 5.10. Effect of shoe upper moisture vapour permeability on galvanic skin resistance.

73

IMPORTANCE OF MOISTURE VAPOUR PERMEABILITY TO FOOT COMFORT AND FOOT HYGIENE

The importance of moisture vapour permeability to foot comfort is supported by actual wear tests conducted on an instrumented treadmill with subjects wearing shoes having uppers of different permeability values. Each subject walked 30 minutes on a treadmill at about 1·7 mph in a controlled body environment and then sat quietly for about two hours. A shoe with upper of different permeability value was used on each foot. All shoes were cross-compared several times in the test (twice in the morning and twice in the afternoon, to average out diurnal variation). Skin wetness was monitored by measuring surface electrical resistance of the skin. Speed of walking was controlled by using a metronome to set cadence.

Skin resistance measurements of replicate experiments on each shoe were averaged and plotted versus time. Fig. 5.10 shows the effects of moisture vapour permeability of shoe uppers on galvanic skin resistance (inversely proportional to skin wetness). The graph is divided into two sections; the first showing the build-up rate of skin wetness during walking and the second section gives the rate of release of moisture while sitting. From these data we can conclude that:

1 During walking, there is little significant difference in skin wetness in closed shoes with different permeabilities. This is attributed to pumping action which occurs mostly through the topline and completely overwhelms differences in permeability. No significant pumping occurs through pores of the upper.
2 During sitting, feet dry at rates in the order predicted by PV values for the uppers.

REFERENCES

1 Hole, L. G., and Butlin, J. G., *J. Brit. Boot and Shoe Inst.*, **15**, No. 4, 79–88 (1968).
2 Pinsky, J., *Modern Plastics*, **34**, 145 (1957).
3 Lasoski, S. W., and Cobbs, W. H., Jr. *J. Polym. Sci.*, **36**, 21–33 (1959).
4 Myers, A. W., Swarc, M., etc. *TAPPI*, **44**, 58–64 (1961).
5 Tuwiner, S. B., 'Diffusion and Membrane Technology', Reinhold Publishing Co., New York, (1962).
6 Barrer, R. M., 'Diffusion in and Through Solids', Cambridge Univ. Press (1951).

CHAPTER 6

Degradation of the polyurethane component by hydrolysis

L. G. HOLE

INTRODUCTION

THE chemical degradation of various shoe components in wear leading to mechanical failure is not a new phenomenon that has suddenly arisen with the introduction of poromeric shoe upper materials. In leather uppers, hardening and cracking is a common form of failure and this has long been known to be largely due to detannage of the leather by the lactate present in sweat. Leather insoles crack and break up in wear for the same reason. This deterioration, as might be expected, is associated with those people who tend to sweat most heavily through their feet. Those observations that have been made at SATRA on poromeric shoes indicate that a similar degradation problem exists for these new upper materials and that this is also due to foot sweat. In this latter case it is not yet known whether it is the total quantity of sweat that is important or whether degradation is due to some particular constituent in sweat which varies in amount with different individuals, irrespective of the total foot sweat output. What is quite clear, however, is that some poromerics are much more susceptible to chemical attack than others, and in the least stable poromeric materials the breakdown can be serious and premature and is almost certain to lead to a complaint by a proportion of customers.

In this paper the chemical structure, and hydrolysis susceptible components, of a poromeric upper material are outlined. Previous work on the causes and possible mechanisms of polymer degradation is considered as these relate to polyurethanes. Evidence of failure of polyurethanes in footwear uppers is given and attempts to simulate this failure in the laboratory are described. Reference is made to the possible influence of various sweat and sebum* components on polymer breakdown.

The application of Boltzmann's superposition principle to the prediction of polyurethane stability in service is outlined and the experimental results for two poromerics are reported. The apparent activation energy for polymer degradation of the polyurethane in these poromerics has also been determined.

---

* Sebum is the fatty material produced by the sebaceous glands in the skin.

CONSTITUENTS OF A POROMERIC SUSCEPTIBLE TO CHEMICAL ATTACKS

Basically most present poromerics are made of polyurethane elastomers (polyester and polyether urethanes are used by different manufacturers) together with various textile fibres, e.g. Terylene or Dacron (polyester), nylon, polypropylene and viscose rayon. Most are multi-layer structures with the urethane-impregnated textile component forming a flexible but mechanically strong substrate. This latter provides the carrier for the microporous urethane top layer which usually has embossed upon it a simulated grain pattern. The microporous layer contains pigments, amongst other things, but no fibrous mechanical reinforcement. A variety of structures within these described limits are used in the various commercial materials and some typical ones are shown diagrammatically in Fig. 6.1.

The microporous top layer (grain) is of more uniform structure than the polyurethane in the substrate and the strains imposed upon it in wear tend to be more severe. It is not surprising that degradation is first apparent in this region of a poromeric, and most of the work reported here relates to the stability of the microporous layers in poromerics. The non-polyurethane components, e.g. Terylene fibres, etc, are relatively more stable to hydrolysis than the elastomer and are not considered further.

One other point concerns the mechanical breakdown that poromerics undergo when flexed. In wear both breakdown processes, i.e. mechanical and chemical, proceed simultaneously but overall performance tends to be complicated by considerable interaction between the mechanical and chemical effects. As chemical attack on the elastomer proceeds the mechanical properties deteriorate rapidly.

CAUSES OF POLYURETHANE BREAKDOWN

Various phenomena that are known to cause deterioration in the physical properties of polymers are given in Table 6.1.

Table 6.1. Natural effects which cause polymer degradation

Mechanical fatigue
Hydrolysis
Heat
Oxidation
Ozonolysis
Ultra-violet light
High energy radiation (background radioactivity, cosmic radiation).

As has been mentioned earlier, there is considerable interaction between mechanical fatigue and the various chemical effects listed, and although this must be kept in mind, no mechanical fatigue effects as such are dealt with in this paper. Heat is italicized because of its overall influence on all the other degrading factors mentioned. Heat

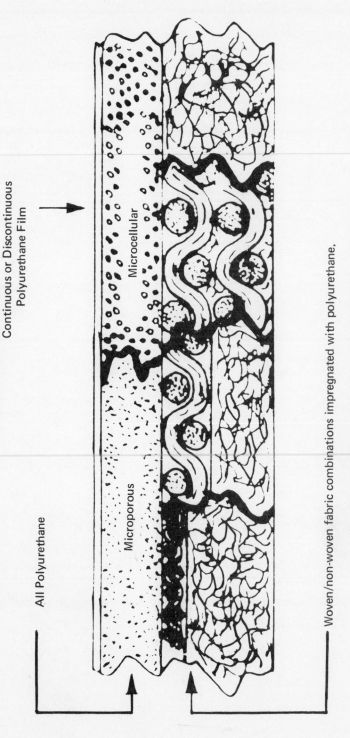

POROMERICS (PERMEABLE)

Continuous or Discontinuous Polyurethane Film

All Polyurethane

Microporous

Microcellular

Woven/non-woven fabric combinations impregnated with polyurethane.

Fig. 6.1. Typical cross-sections of various poromeric materials.

alone will cause polymer breakdown at high temperatures and a good example is that of polyvinyl chloride which degrades when heated, with the evolution of hydrogen chloride, e.g. when accidentally overheated in screw injection-moulding machines. Of more general importance, however, is the increase in the rate of attack on the polymer by moisture, oxygen, ozone, etc, as the temperature is raised.

With poromerics (based upon polyurethanes) the most important forms of attack are:

(i) Hydrolysis resulting from the high humidity caused by sweat and rain and storage in damp conditions. Hydrolysis will be promoted by various substances present in small amounts in sweat, together with the degradation products of these substances caused by microbiological reactions on the skin, e.g. urea producing ammonia.

(ii) Oxidation and ozonolysis effects with the accompanying direct influence of ultra-violet radiation. With polyurethanes, however, these are probably of secondary importance compared with hydrolysis, especially when the latter is promoted as mentioned above. There are of course interaction effects between moisture, heat, oxidation and UV light.

The effect of UV light in practice is believed to be relatively small, however because shoes are not normally worn in direct sunlight for long periods. Also the polymer invariably contains absorptive pigments, e.g. carbon black, which will confine UV attack to the outside surface of the poromeric. However, in the footwear examined at SATRA, the polymer breakdown has quite clearly started deep inside the microporous layer and not at the outside surface.

High energy radiation is a different matter in that penetration right through the poromeric will take place, but since the evidence in support of hydrolysis as the primary cause is so clear, all radiation effects are believed to play only a minor role.

All these types of reaction process will cause bond rupture in the polymer, and depending upon the bond attacked, this rupture may lead either to chain scission or possibly breakage of crosslinks, or a combination of both. It is also possible that the breakdown products may crosslink scissioned polymer molecules.

The two basic types of molecule used in polyurethanes are esters and ethers with the urethane group forming the linkages both along and between chains (the former are predominant in the relatively thermoplastic polymers used in poromerics). The urea, biuret and allophanate groups also occur as linkages and their relative amounts will depend upon the type and method of manufacture of the polyurethane.

The linkage most readily attacked and scissioned will depend upon the bond strengths in each group and Table 6.2 gives the values for the specific types of bond involved.

78

Some typical bonds as found in polyurethanes are:

Polymer group		Known and possible products of hydrolysis
R.CO.OR′ Ester	H_2O $\longrightarrow$	R.COOH + R′.OH
R.O.R′. Ether	H_2O $\longrightarrow$	R.OH + R′.OH
R.NH.CO.O.R′ Urethane	H_2O $\longrightarrow$	R.NH$_2$ + R′.OH + CO$_2$ ↑
R.NH.CO.NH.R′ Urea	H_2O $\longrightarrow$	R.NH$_2$ + R′.NH$_2$ + CO$_2$ ↑
R″ RNH.CO.N.CO.NHR′ Biuret	H_2O $\longrightarrow$	RNH.CO.NHR″ + CO$_2$ ↑ + R′NH$_2$
R″ RNH.CO.N.CO.OR′ Allophanate	H_2O $\longrightarrow$	RNH.CO.NHR″ + CO$_2$ ↑ + R′OH

Table 6.2. Bond dissociation energies

Bond	Dissociation energy (kcal/mol)
C − N	49–60
C − C	59–70
C − O	70–75
N − H	84–97

These values suggest that ether and ester linkages should be equally stable; however, because of interactions with adjoining atoms, the bond stability will vary and it is well known that polyurethanes with ether links are much more stable to hydrolysis than those with ester links. The graph in Fig. 6.2 shows the results given by P. Wright [1] on the relative resistance to hydrolysis of polyester and polyether based polyurethanes when immersed in water at 50°C and 70°C over periods of several months. These results indicate that even at the relatively low temperature of 50°C the polyester studied was degraded fairly rapidly. The dissociation energy of the carbon-nitrogen bond is by far the lowest so that scission at the urethane linkage would appear to be the main cause of degradation. Wright's results indicate, however, that there must be some interaction leading to bond stabilization when the various groups are combined in a polymer; this leading to an increase in stability of the C–N link to a level above that of the ester, resulting in scission at the ester link. Alternatively the ether may stabilize the C–N link, whilst the ester does not: in this case scission would occur at the urethane link. To clarify this it would be of interest to determine the nature of the end groups in the degraded polymers to establish whether they result from scission of the R.NH.CO.OR', the R.CO.OR' or the R.O.R' links.

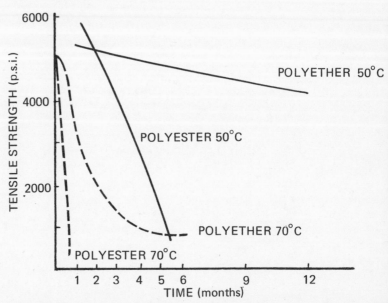

HYDROLYSIS OF POLYESTER AND POLYETHER POLYURETHANES (WATER IMMERSION AT 50° AND 70°C)

Fig. 6.2. Graph showing ether-v-ester polyurethane stability [1].

The possible influence of aromatic, urea, biuret and allophanate groups, which may be present in the polymer, upon stability must also be considered because of the relative molecular cohesive energies (Table 6.3) of these groups, some of which are high compared with the C–O–C link present in esters and ethers. It has been shown by Kogon [2], however, that the biuret and allophanate links themselves are easily broken at temperatures of 100-120°C: the presence of moisture and catalysts makes these links possible scission points at lower temperatures. Similarly the biuret and allophanate groups are rapidly attacked and scissioned by amines (and presumably ammonia) at 150°C [3, 4] and this reaction may also contribute to slow degradation at the lower temperature of the human foot.

The stability of these polyurethanes is also complicated by a variety of other factors such as the influence of degradation catalysts in the polymer, the precursors of which may have been deliberately added during manufacture for some other specific but quite different purpose. The degradation reaction may also be autocatalytic. Catalysed reactions are certainly involved and some work has been done on the use of the carbodiimides and oxazolidines as stabilizers. These substances behave as scavengers for carboxylic acids [5] and since

Table 6.3. Molecular cohesive energy of groups present in polyurethanes

			Molecular cohesive energy (kcal/mol)
Hydrocarbon	–	–CH$_2$–	–	0·68
Ether	–	–C–O–C–	–	1·00
Ester	–	–C–O–C– $\parallel$ O	–	2·90
Aromatic		⟨O⟩	–	3·90
Urethane	–	NH.CO.O–	–	8·74
Urea	–	NH.CO.NH–	–	>8·74

these latter can be the products of, and catalysts for, autocatalytic degradation reactions in polyurethanes, the presence of a carbodiimide will improve the stability to hydrolysis of a urethane polymer. Neumann, Holtschmidt and Kallert [5] have shown that carbodiimide acts as a stabilizer for a urethane polymer over periods of up to 50 days during which it was exposed to an atmosphere of 90% relative humidity at 70°C. The fall in the tensile strength of the polymer with and without the carbodiimide stabilizer is shown in Fig. 6.3. Metzger and Cross [6]

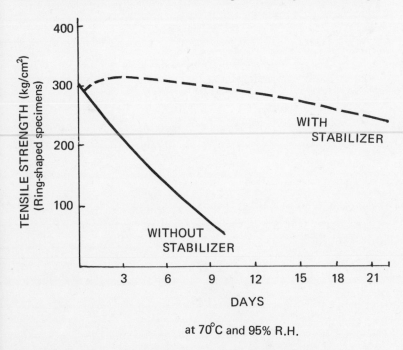

at 70°C and 95% R.H.

Fig. 6.3. This shows the effect of carbodiimide when added to polyurethane to provide improved resistance to hydrolysis [5]. The polymer is a peroxide cross-linked urethane elastomer containing 15% HAF black. 3% of polycarbodiimide added to stabilise the polymer.

examined a series of imino-oxazolidine derivatives and showed that various substituents in the 2-imino position influenced the degree of stabilization obtained in the polyurethanes when exposed to saturated steam at 100°C. The time to failure increased by factors of 1·2 to 2·5 with the imino-oxazolidines present.

The polyurethanes are different from some other polymers in their property of higher water absorption and transmission. The absorption values are higher than, for example, the water absorption of Terylene. Thus another factor in hydrolytic degradation is the influence of rate of diffusion of water into the polymer on the degradation rate of reaction. Lasoski and Cobbs [7] have suggested that diffusion of water into polyethylene terephthalate (Mylar*) films occurs in the amorphous regions of the polymer and they assumed that hydrolysis occurs in these regions rather than the crystalline portion. Most of the polyurethanes used in poromerics have a large amorphous component and because of their microporous (cellular) structure the polymer is effectively a film. The cell wall thickness in a poromeric is of similar dimensions to that studied by Lasoski and Cobbs with Mylar Golike and Lasoski [8] have shown that diffusion of water into polyethelene terephthalate is the rate limiting factor in hydrolysis and that the reaction rate and diffusion coefficient were related by

$$\frac{n}{a} = kC \frac{\tanh \sqrt{\left(\frac{kal}{D}\right)}}{\sqrt{\left(\frac{kal}{D}\right)}} t = k't \tag{1}$$

n = moles of ester linkages hydrolysed per mole of polymer
a = moles of ester linkages initially present per mole of polymer
k = specific reaction rate constant
D = diffusion coefficient
l = one-half the film thickness
t = time
$k't = kCt$ where $C = (b - n)$
b = moles of water initially present per mole of polymer
C = water concentration at the film surface.

Since the water concentration is effectively constant under the experimental conditions, C is taken as the effective water concentration, the reaction kinetics being of a pseudo first-order type,

i.e. $$\frac{dn}{dt} = kC(a - n) \tag{2}$$

The amorphous fraction in the Mylar used by Lasoski and Cobbs was 0·53. It is probable that in the group of polyurethanes being considered here both the amorphous component and the diffusion rate for water is higher than in Mylar, thus in very thin films such as could occur in microporous urethanes diffusion might not be the rate limiting factor. When examining thicker solid specimens, however, e.g. 0·5 and 1·0 mm, it may be necessary to take account of the diffusion coefficient.

* Du Pont's polyester film (Dacron).

A large number of imine groups are present in urethane polymers and since each one of these groups can readily take part in hydrogen bonding between adjacent inter and intrachain groups, the number and nature of the groups involved may affect the hydrolytic stability of the polymers. As the number of moles of urethane per mole of polymer increases, so does the number of hydrogen bonds, the greatest number forming when the number of polymer units between each urethane group is even according to Bayer's zigzag rule [9]. That interchain hydrogen bonds can easily form in urethane polymers is shown in the photograph (Fig. 6.4, Plate 11) of a molecular model of a section of two polyurethane chains.

Formation of a hydrogen bond at an imine group in the urethane link might make the latter more open to attack due to the electron delocalisation in the modified imino and adjacent groups, i.e.

$$OH^{\ominus} \quad H_3^{\oplus}O$$

$$R.NH - C^{\delta+} - O^{\delta-} - R \text{ Chain A}$$

$$\| \atop O^{\delta-}$$

$$\vdots \quad \Big\} \text{ Hydrogen bond}$$

$$H^{\delta+}$$

$$| \atop R - N^{\delta-} - C^{\delta+} - O - RH^{\delta+} \text{ Chain B}$$

$$\| \atop O$$

$$H_3^{\oplus}O \quad OH^{\ominus}$$

According to Bayer's zigzag rule this would suggest that for a given urethane polymer, improved resistance to hydrolysis might result from having an odd number of polymer units between urethane linkages if the hydrogen bonds do make a urethane group more susceptible to attack. The physical result of degradation in a polyurethane can take two forms; first, loss of elasticity and embrittlement due to breakdown of the main chains, or alternatively, softening due to breakdown of the urethane crosslinks between chains. Only in one poromeric has the author observed the latter phenomenon and this occurred during the early stages of controlled hydrolysis. At higher temperatures but under otherwise identical conditions the more common reduction in elasticity and embrittlement appeared. These effects are shown diagrammatically in Fig. 6.5.

FAILURE OF POROMERIC FOOTWEAR IN WEAR

The study of polyurethane stability at SATRA was the direct result of poromeric shoe upper failures returned by shoe manufacturing members of the Association. During the past four or five years, other development work in industry and at SATRA on polyurethane foam soles had been bedevilled by premature cracking and undesirable levels of water absorption when in wear. It is clear that both upper and sole materials require urethane polymer systems of maximum stability to hydrolysis whilst retaining all the necessary properties for satisfactory performance in footwear, e.g. flexibility.

BREAKDOWN OF POLYMER STRUCTURE

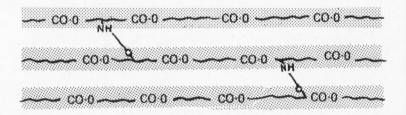

BREAKING MAIN CHAINS: LOSS OF ELASTICITY ETC.

SEPARATION OF MAIN CHAINS: SOFTENING

VALENCE BOND FAILURES IN POLYURETHANE CHAINS

Fig. 6.5. Mode of breakdown of polymer structure.

One of the first poromeric shoes to be sent to SATRA showing polyurethane degradation is shown in Fig. 6.6.

This shoe is representative of numbers of degraded shoes received from three large British shoe manufacturers. In all cases the failure has occurred primarily in the microporous top layer. The embrittlement of the polymer, which has occurred without exception, has resulted in initial cracking followed by flaking away of the top layer from the substrate. In the more severe cases cracking and breaking of the impregnant polymer in the substrate has also take place. A significant feature of the damaged shoes is the coincidence of foot pressure points with the degraded region, e.g. where toes have pressed against the upper. In the same shoes the central vamp areas that have been subjected to severe flexing have remained undamaged. This suggests that direct liquid sweat and sebum transfer to the poromeric, such as will occur at pressure points, may be the main cause of rapid failure of the polymer. In other shoes failure has occurred in the upper material regions close to the sole and this is quite consistent with the absorption of liquid sweat into the insole, which then permeates to the upper-insole junction and so into the upper material.

Most of the sweat taken up by the relatively undamaged flexing region of the upper is from water vapour, thus indicating that the rate of degradation of the polymer is substantially affected by one or more of the non-aqueous components of sweat which only reach the polymer when direct liquid sweat transfer is possible.

With a shoe a considerable variety of materials can come into contact with the upper from outside, e.g. urine, oil, etc. and urine contamination has always been a considerable problem with leather, which is severely degraded when urine is present. Most people, however, do not have these problems where various circumstances cause active chemicals to come into contact with the outside of their shoes. Microscopic examination of cross-sections of the damaged areas of poromeric shows (Fig. 6.7) that degradation starts in the region of the top layer adjacent to the substrate and gradually works through to the 'grain' surface of the microporous layer.

On the assumption that the degradation problem was one of hydrolysis some preliminary experiments were done in which new material was exposed to steam at 120°C for up to 12 hours. A cross-section of this laboratory degraded material (Fig. 6.8) shows that failure of the microporous layer starts close to the 'grain' surface and works in. This is as might be expected because the steam would be present at all the surfaces of the poromeric during the hydrolysing treatment; thus degradation would be fairly uniform throughout the material. Failure occurs near the outside because of the higher strains in these regions when the material is bent as in Fig. 6.8. Samples of the steam degraded material were also repeatedly extended by a hemisphere of ¾-inch diameter in an attempt to simulate the pressure of a toe on the upper during walking. A sample treated in this way is shown in Fig. 6.9 and its appearance is identical to the toe pressure point areas on the degraded shoes.

Five of the damaged shoes were chosen for preliminary chemical analysis, the vamp areas being cut from the shoes as shown in Fig. 6.10. The results of the analysis are given in Table 6.4.

None of the results are very conclusive, the main indication being that in wear the pH of the poromeric can fall by as much as 1·25 pH units. The significance of the high total water solubles and potassium and chloride values for the tongue areas (samples 1C and 2C, see also Fig. 6.10) is not clear because this would indicate that maximum degradation should occur in this region, whereas in fact this was the least affected area of the vamps. Unfortunately an analysis for ammonia and urea was not done on these vamps and, as will be seen later, these figures would have had greater interest. This poromeric is more susceptible to breakdown in the laboratory at alkaline pHs, i.e. pH 8-9 compared with pH 3, and this is also supported by the results for vamp No. 5, which shows extensive damage, the shaded areas having a pH close to and slightly above that of the original material.

LABORATORY SIMULATION OF CHEMICAL DEGRADATION IN WEAR

The medical and other literature records a large number of materials as occurring on the human skin from sweat glands and other sources.

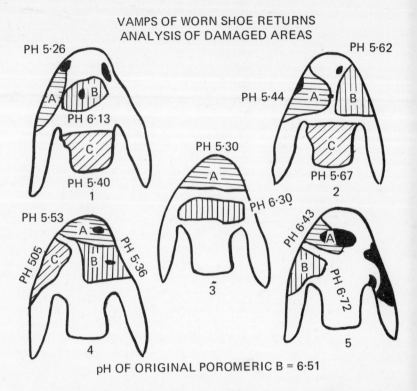

Fig. 6.10. The poromeric B vamps were cut from five damaged shoes. The embrittled and cracked places are shown by the dark areas. The shaded areas are those cut out for individual chemical analysis, the results of which were inconclusive except that all but one of the areas showed a reduction in pH compared with the original poromeric.

Most of these substances can be transferred to footwear via the hose, and their number and type will be extended as microbiological and other changes take place on the skin surface, and in the hose and shoe. Some of the substances likely to be active in the degradation of polyurethanes are listed in Table 6.5; a number of these have been shown to be present in worn footwear [10].

The wide range of values for the various substances in sweat is very significant with regard to the incidence of wearers that cause degradation of poromerics. It is not unexpected that persons producing the larger amounts of nitrogenous substances should cause degradation of polyurethanes because of the possible reactions between ammonia and amines and the polymer as well as pH effects. The shoe analyses by Pettit [10] are particularly interesting because of the relatively large amounts of sweat residue that concentrate in the shoe uppers and other components in wear. (Pettit has taken an average value for chloride of 320 mg/100 g sweat from the various published results (see Kuno [11]), then corrected all the analytical data for leather uppers to the same assumed chloride value.) Clearly any study of shoe polymer degradation must include an examination of the effect of these active contaminants coming from the sweat and sebum of the wearer.

The two substances squalene (molecule contains six isoprene units in open chain and thus is structurally related to the steroids) and oleic acid are important because of their known degradation of polyurethane elastomers of the type used in the elastic supporting bands of underwear garments [12].

Human sebum contains between 3·3–11·7% of squalene and an average of about 10% free oleic acid [18, 19].

As a preliminary experiment in controlled polymer degradation four treatments were chosen:

(a) Steam at 120°C (15 psi) for 12 hours.
(b) Water at 90°C, pH = 5·5 for 64 hours.
(c) Lactic acid 100 mg per 100 ml. 90°C, pH = 2·6 for 64 hours.
(d) Ammonia   5 mg per 100 ml. 90°C, pH = 9·6 for 64 hours.

The pHs of the solutions b, c and d after the 64 hours polymer hydrolysis were:

b. Water   pH = 8·3
c. Lactic acid pH = 2·8
d. Ammonia   pH = 7·9

After treatment (a) the poromeric was severely degraded: a single slight fold of the material was sufficient to cause the microporous layer to crack (see also Fig. 6.9). Treatment (d) was equally severe on the basis of these fairly crude mechanical tests. There was little difference between (b) and (c) although the sample hydrolysed in plain water was the worse of the two; this is very likely related to the considerable rise

Table 6.4. Chemical analysis of damaged uppers

Reference to Fig. 6.10.	pH	% Total water solubles	Potassium as ppm of the material (poromeric B)	Chloride as ppm of the material (poromeric B)
1 A	5·26	0·7	80	600
1 B	6·13	–	–	–
1 C	5·40	1·4	170	2,800
2 A	5·44	1·2	50	1,000
2 B	5·62	0·8	30	700
2 C	5·67	1·9	130	2,000
3 A	5·30	1·4	60	500
3 B	6·30	0·8	110	900
4 A	5·53	1·5	100	1,200
4 B	5·36	0·6	70	1,300
4 C	5·05	0·5	40	1,300
5 A	6·43	–	–	–
5 B	6·72	–	–	–
Original material	6·51	0·04	3	80

Table 6.5. Sweat residues in worn shoe uppers
(milligrams per 100 g sweat)

	Active material	SATRA worn leather uppers analysis [10]	Analysis of sweat [1?
Protein metabolites	Urea nitrogen	61	11·9-29·2
	Ammonia nitrogen	17	1-7·2
Glucose metabolites	Lactate	610	100-300
	Pyruvic acid	–	0·9-6·9
	Glucose	–	1-11
	Chloride	320 (assumed)	320 (195-995)
	Potassium	270	20-100
	Sodium	197	67-170
	Squalene	–	present in sebum
	Oleic acid	–	present in sebum
	pH	–	5·5-7·8

in pH of the water during the hydrolysis presumably due to amine degradation products from the polymer.

All of the samples from these experiments as well as virgin material and material from damaged shoes were extracted with dimethyl formamide and the extracted clarified polymer examined in an infra-red spectrometer (Unicam SP 200) by transmission. The results, together with those for flexing test [13], are given in Table 6.6.

The appearance of the extracted polymer indicates a reduction in molecular weight and further work to measure these changes using viscometry, osmometry and light scattering is planned. The IR results are inconclusive and this technique seems to be of limited value compared with others for this particular degree of polymer change. The flexing test, although only qualitative, is clearly able to detect what appear to be fairly subtle chemical changes in the polymer that are shown up by large changes in mechanical properties. Some idea of the difference in stability of five poromerics to the steam hydrolysis conditions (8 hours) may be seen in Fig. 6.11. The influence of time of treatment in steam at 120°C can also be seen in Fig. 6.12, where the same poromeric was hydrolysed for 2, 4, 8 and 16 hours. In all cases (Figs 6.11 and 6.12) the samples were flexed 1 000 000 times in the SATRA Flex Test STM 101 at 20°C after reconditioning to 65% RH/20°C, following hydrolysis treatment.

These preliminary tests have shown quite clearly that a controlled hydrolysis test with a conveniently short testing time (hours compared with weeks or months at normal temperatures) is possible with reasonably good comparison between the type of degradation in wear and in the test. Ammonia in amounts comparable with that commonly found in worn leather uppers is shown to cause very severe degradation at 90°C and similar results were obtained when urea solutions at 90°C were used. Tensile samples hydrolysed with ammonia and urea solutions are shown in Fig. 6.13.

The pH was measured during the hydrolysis with ammonia and urea solutions and the results are shown in Table 6.7.

With ammonia the pH changes suggest an initial reaction with the polymer causing a fall in pH, subsequent reactions perhaps with the release of amines resulting in an increase in pH. Tests showed that the urea was breaking down with the gradual formation of ammonia and the amount of the latter in the solution increased throughout the 64 hours although the amounts were small. (After 32 and 64 hours the ammonia in the treatment solution could be detected by smell.)

Table 6.6. Degraded poromeric: Flexing tests and IR analysis of polyurethane microporous layer

Sample history	Appearance of extracted polymer	Infra-red analysis	Flexing test crack grade:* No. of flexes (STM 101 at 20°C)
Untreated	Film: Matt finish	Control	A: 1,000,000
Lactic acid pH = 2·6 90°C : 64 hours	do.	Little change	A: 10,000 C: 100,000
Uncracked region of damaged shoe	Film: Slightly matt finish	Reduction in backbone ester but no —COOH formation	Similar to lactic acid (c) and water (d) treatments
Water pH = 5·5 90°C : 64 hours	Film: Shiny finish	Little change	B: 1,000 C: 10,000
Steam: 120°C 12 hours	Wax: no film	Reduction in backbone ester but no —COOH formation	C: 1
Ammonia pH = 9·6 90°C : 64 hours	Wax: no film	do.	C: 1

* The crack grades are— A: fine cracks confined to the surface skin of the microporous layer; B: cracks that have penetrated into the microporous layer; C: cracks that have reached the microporous layer—substrate junction and beyond; D: cracks penetrating right through the material.

89

Table 6.7. pH of ammonia and urea solutions after hydrolysis of poromeric B for the times shown

Hydrolysis time (hours)	pH at 20°C			
	Ammonia solution 10 mg*	Ammonia solution 1 mg*	Urea solution 4.7 mg*	Urea solution 23.4 mg*
0	10.3	9.7	5.6	5.7
4	–	–	7.1	7.3
8	7.5	6.8	7.4	8.2
16	8.6	7.2	8.0	8.4
32	8.4	7.7	8.5	8.7
64	–	6.8	8.3	8.6

* The weights in milligrams are the weights of nitrogen from ammonia and urea respectively, present in 100 ml of solution. These figures compare with the values given in Table 6.5.

This latter work has clearly shown the very important influence of sweat components upon the chemical breakdown of the polyurethanes at present used in some poromerics. As will be seen later controlled hydrolysis with water provides useful means of estimating the stability and likely performance of a poromeric in wear. Because of the catalytic effects of sweat components, however, the results obtained for water hydrolysis are likely to be optimistic (one effect of sweat ingredients may be to change the ranking order). The activation energy values and predicted degradation rate in water will be substantially reduced by these catalysts and further work is in progress to quantify these effects.

THE SUPERPOSITION PRINCIPLE FOR WEAR LIFE PREDICTION

Preliminary experiments indicate that the use of the time-temperature superposition principle (see Leaderman, Ferry, R. W. Hefty [14-16]) might be possible for the construction of a master curve for the prediction of degradation rate of polyurethanes at ambient temperatures. To do hydrolytic stability tests on polyurethanes at ambient temperatures would require treatment times much too long to be of much practical use either to the polymer chemists making poromerics or to the shoe manufacturer seeking confidence in the footwear he is marketing.

Although polymer degradation as studied here is an irreversible reaction we have assumed that the kinetic principles of reversible reactions are applicable. Experimental results reported here and elsewhere are in fact consistent with these principles.

Boltzmann showed that $k = A \exp -\dfrac{E}{RT}$ \hfill (3)

k = Boltzmann's constant (specific reaction rate: see below)

A = the frequency factor, i.e. total frequency of encounters between two reactive molecules irrespective of whether they have sufficient energy to react or not.

E = Arrhenius activation energy

R = universal gas constant

T = absolute temperature

Taking logarithms, equation (3) becomes

$$\log_e k = -\frac{E}{RT} + \text{constant} \tag{4}$$

A similar expression has been obtained empirically confirming the validity of equation (3), where k = specific reaction rate thus showing the relationship between the latter and $A \exp - E/RT$. This provides a pathway to the experimental evaluation of the activation energy E by the measurement of k for the polymer degradation reaction.

The significance of the activation energy is that it provides a measure of polymer stability. Reactions having activation energies of about 15-20 kcal will take place at room temperature and it is obviously desirable that the polyurethanes in poromerics have values well above this, e.g. 30-35 kcal, for satisfactory stability in wear.

The value of E is lowered by catalysts and this is all the more reason why high activation energy values are desirable. A polymer with an activation energy of 18 kcal, such as the material poromeric B as was used in the damaged shoe (Fig. 6.6), might be reduced to dangerously low levels by catalysts; indeed it appears that this may be so with the degraded footwear.

If it is assumed that polymer degradation by hydrolysis is a first-order reaction (see Golike and Lasoski [8]) then

$$\text{rate of degradation:} \ \frac{dn}{dt} = k\,(a - n) \tag{5}$$

(See equation (1) for meaning of parameters.)

In practice equation (5) is probably an over-simplification because the products of polymer degradation will affect the specific reaction rate, the degradation probably becoming autocatalytic.

The rate of degradation will then become [17]

$$\frac{dn}{dt} = k_1\,(a - n)C + k_2\,(a - n)n \tag{6}$$

$$= (k_1 C + k_2 n)\,(a - n) \tag{7}$$

Upon integration

$$k_1 C + k_2 a = \frac{1}{t}\,\log_e \frac{a(k_1 C + k_2 n)}{k_1 C(a - n)} \tag{8}$$

91

Where C is the amount of catalyst originally present and n that produced by the degradation reaction and where the initial catalyst C is a different substance to that produced by the polymer degradation n.

The work at SATRA suggests that poromeric degradation under laboratory conditions is probably autocatalytic, so that equation (8) should be obeyed. In the present work with distilled water, equation (5) has been assumed. However, equation (8) will be tested in future experiments with, for example, ammonia present as the initial catalyst C.

The specific reaction rate k is dependent upon the absolute temperature (see equation (3)), thus if a polymer is degraded in water at different temperatures, say 70, 90 and 120°C, then the time for the polymer to reach a certain stage of degradation will vary, the longest time being required at the lowest temperature. The elapsed time t to reach a certain level of degradation is inversely proportional to the rate constant k. (This follows on integrating equation (5).)

$$t \propto k^{-1} \tag{9}$$

Thus
$$\frac{t_1}{t_2} = \frac{k_2}{k_1} = a_T \tag{10}$$

where t_1/t_2 is the ratio of the reference time to reach a certain level of degradation at the temperature chosen for the master curve, to the time required to reach the same level of degradation at the other reaction temperatures. a_T is a scale factor, one of which will be obtained for each degradation temperature. It is plotted against $1/T$ to obtain the Arrhenius plot (Fig. 6.20) and subsequently used with the master curve for the prediction of time scales to forecast the time for any chosen level of degradation to be reached at normal room and foot temperatures.

It follows from equation (3) and equation (10) that

$$a_T = \frac{\exp{-\dfrac{E}{RT_2}}}{\exp{-\dfrac{E}{RT_1}}} \tag{11}$$

Where E = apparent activation energy.

From (11)
$$\log_e a_T = \frac{-E}{RT_2} - \left(-\frac{E}{RT_1}\right) \tag{12}$$

Hence
$$E = \frac{R \log_e a_T}{(T_1^{-1} - T_2^{-1})} \tag{13}$$

Because
$$\log_e a_T = \log_e \frac{(a_{T_2})}{(a_{T_1})} \quad \text{(see equation (10))} \tag{14}$$

where $(a_{T_1}) = 1$

then it can be shown that [16]

$$E = - \frac{4 \cdot 576 \log_{10}\left(\dfrac{a_{T_2}}{a_{T_1}}\right)}{(T_2^{-1} - T_1^{-1})} \qquad (15)$$

from which the apparent activation energy E is readily calculated from the scale factors at any given level of degradation and the corresponding absolute temperatures used for the polymer degradation.

A preliminary experiment was done on four poromerics.

1-cm wide strips of suitable length to provide a gauge length of 10 cm were cut from the complete material and from the separated microporous top layer. These samples were hydrolysed in steam at 120°C (15 psi) for 2, 4, 8 and 16 hours and then reconditioned for 48 hours at 65% RH at

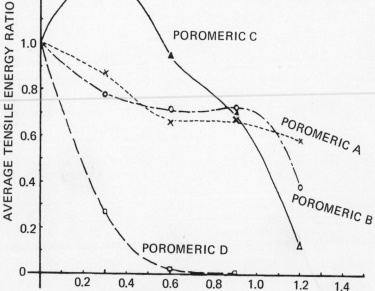

Fig. 6.14. Results for four poromerics showing the change in tensile energy with hydrolysis time. The result for poromeric C is interesting: the increase in tensile energy to break introduced during the early stages of the hydrolysis treatment is possibly due to an increase in the degree of crosslinking in the polymer.

20°C. The ratios of tensile energy to break of the hydrolysed specimens to·the tensile energy to break of the untreated control specimens are shown plotted against hydrolysis time in Fig. 6.14 (complete material) and Fig. 6.15 (microporous layer). (The tensile energy of the specimens was measured on an Instron Tensile Testing machine.)

RATIO OF AVERAGE TENSILE ENERGY v LOG_{10} OF THE
DEGRADATION TIME (MICROPOROUS LAYER)

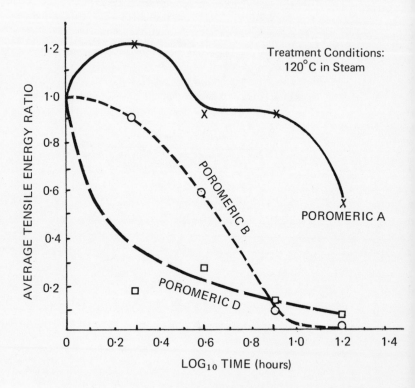

Fig. 6.15. The microporous layers for poromerics A, B, and D shown in Fig. 6.14. It is significant that the microporous layer of A shows a similar increase in tensile energy during the early stages of treatment to that shown by the whole poromeric C, this latter material having no fibrous component in its structure. Further work is being done to find if the less hydrolysis-resistant polymers in these graphs undergo a similar increase in strength at shorter hydrolysis times, i.e. less than 2 hours.

The results show that degradation of the whole material or component parts of it, is readily determined by this tensile technique. For various reasons subsequent work reported here has been done on the microporous layer only.

In a typical experiment to determine the apparent activation energy and

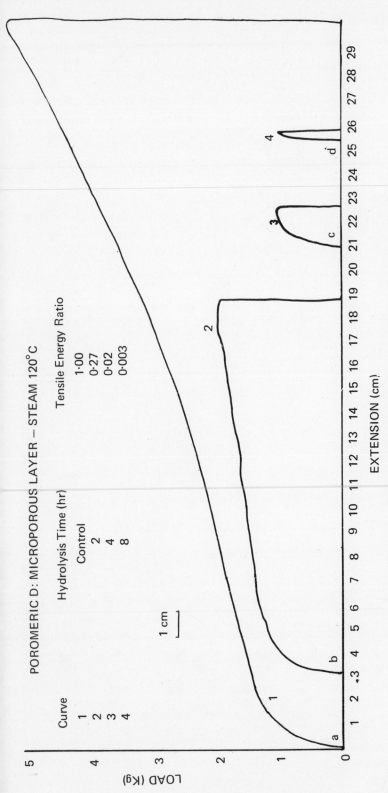

Fig. 6.16. This shows the stress-strain plots as obtained on the Instron for the microporous layer of poromeric D. The hydrolysis time corresponding to each plot is shown, the area within the curve being a measure of the tensile energy of the material. This polymer is not very resistant to hydrolysis at 120°C in steam. For clarity the zero points have been deliberately moved so that each tensile curve may be seen; strictly points a, b, c and d should all be at the same origin.

95

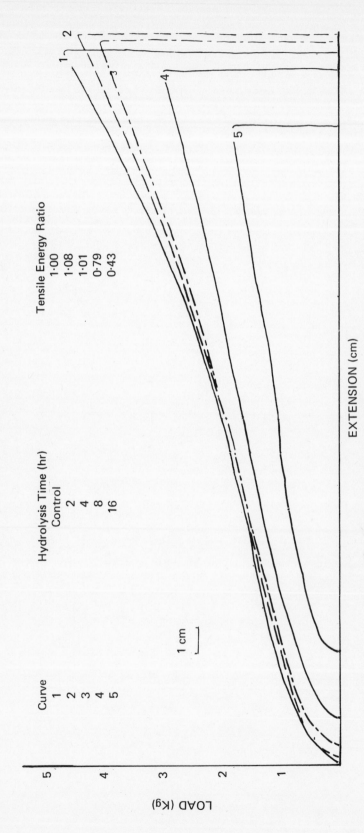

Fig. 6.17. This is similar to Fig. 6.16 but showing the results for a much more hydrolysis-resistant polyurethane (poromeric A).

96

predict degradation rate of a poromeric at ambient temperatures the hydrolysis was done on four groups of test pieces as follows:

    (i) 120°C steam (15 psi) for 2, 4, 8, 16 hours
    (ii) 90°C immersed in distilled water for 8, 16, 32, 64 hours
    (iii) 70°C immersed in distilled water for 8, 16, 32, 64 hours
    (iv) Controls—untreated.

After treatment the samples were reconditioned for 48 hours at 65% RH–20°C, and the tensile energy to break the samples were measured on an Instron Tensile Machine. A visual indication of the differences in stability of different poromerics (microporous layer) is shown in Fig. 6.16 and Fig. 6.17.

A 25% reduction in tensile energy as indicated by the dotted line in Fig. 6.18 was taken as the degradation reference level from which the scale factors in Table 6.8 were obtained.

Table 6.8. Time to produce a 25% reduction in tensile energy and the corresponding scale factors (poromeric D)

Temperature, °C	t, hours	a_T
120	1	10·5
90	10·5	1
70	44	0·24

The master curve for poromeric D based upon degradation at 90°C is shown in Fig. 6.19.

Thus Fig. 6.18 suggests that 10 hours at 120°C in steam will cause a 25% fall in tensile energy of this poromeric microporous layer. The 10 hours at 120°C corresponds with 7½ weeks at 32°C and 25 weeks at 20°C to cause the same fall in tensile properties of the polymer in the presence of water. It must be remembered that in wear active substances will be present in addition to water as discussed earlier. These materials will accelerate the degradation of the polymer as has been described and further work is in progress to examine the influence of catalytic substances on the apparent activation energy and predicted wear life of different poromerics.

The well-known Arrhenius plot (Fig. 6.20) is obtained (see equation (13)) where the slope of the line equals $-E/RT$.

The apparent activation energy for scission of the polymer molecule can also be calculated by substitution of the results in Table 6.8 in equation (15). Thus in the case of the poromeric D the value of $E = 18·7$ kcal/mol. The value of E for poromeric F has been determined in the same way and is 15 kcal/mol. These values are low and such reactions will proceed measurably at room temperature.*

---

* The activation energy of hydrogen bond scission is 2 to 12 kcal/mol depending upon adjacent atoms and structure. Thus a polymer with a value of E equal to 15 kcal/mol might not contain covalent crosslinks but depend primarily upon hydrogen bonds for intermolecular cohesion. If this is so it has importance with regard to the heat setting and shape retention properties of such poromerics.

MASTER CURVE FOR POROMERIC D AT 90°C

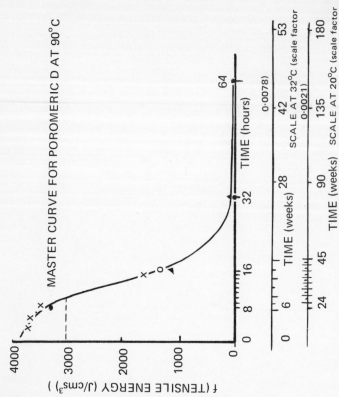

Fig. 6.19. The master curve for the degradation of poromeric D (microporous layer) at 90°C. This was obtained as explained in the text. The predicted life scales for 20° and 32°C have been obtained from the Arrhenius plot (Fig. 6.20) by extrapolating the line to the required temperatures and reading off the corresponding scale factors. The 90°C scale of degradation in this figure being the master scale is, by definition, $a_T = 1$.

This scale is corrected accordingly by the 20° and 32°C scale factors · to produce the two degradation rate scales for these two temperatures, which are measured in 0-180 weeks and 0-53 weeks respectively.

BREAKDOWN OF A MICROPOROUS LAYER AT VARIOUS TEMPERATURES

DEGRADATION—TIME HYDROLYSIS CURVES FOR POROMERIC D

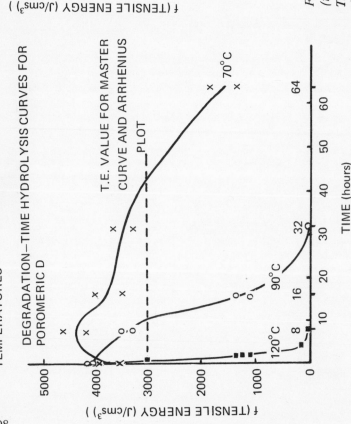

Fig. 6.18. Tensile energy plotted against degradation time. The dotted line corresponds to a 25% fall in strength of the polymer and the scale factors in Table 6.8 corresponds to those points where the dotted line crosses the various curves. For preparation of the master curve (Fig. 6.19) it is usual to choose the lowest temperature that gives an easily measured and convenient rate of degradation. In this experiment 90°C was chosen.

Clearly because of any reduction in E that catalysts will almost certainly cause it must be concluded that these particular poromerics might suffer degradation in wear. Similar measurements on other poromerics have given much higher values–approaching 30 kcal.

That this technique is useful for the prediction of resistance to hydrolysis in wear is shown by the examination of worn shoes. Those poromeric shoes with E values around 15–20 kcal/mol do chemically degrade prematurely in wear (sometimes after as little as about 4 weeks wear) whereas those materials with E above 30 kcal/mol have shown little or no signs of chemical degradation after months of wear. These latter materials tend to suffer from mechanical fatigue, although after lengthy wear on heavy sweaters there is some evidence for the influence of chemical factors.

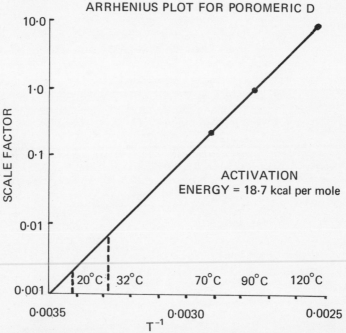

Fig. 6.20. The scale factor plotted against T^{-1} produces the Arrhenius plot straight line for poromeric D. The microporous layers of poromerics have given good results in this method. The scale factors for other temperatures are obtained from this line and applied to the master curve for the prediction of degradation rate at lower temperatures. The slope of the line is equal to E/RT thus providing a means of calculating the activation energy for molecular scission of the material.

In some cases it may be impracticable for a poromerics manufacturer to use more stable polymers in his material and the use of chemical stabilizers may be of considerable value. SATRA is actively studying this latter approach and it is hoped that improved durability in poromeric footwear will result from this work.

I would like to thank Mr L. W. Birch and Mr A. McIntyre who have been responsible for the experimental work from which the results for chemical degradation reported here have been obtained.

REFERENCES

1 P. Wright, *Aircraft Engineering,* p. 20. November (1967).
2 I. C. Kogon, *J. Org. Chem.* **24**, 83 (1959).
3 R. G. Arnold, J. A. Nelson and J. J. Verbanc. American Chemical Society Rubber Division Meeting. May 16-18 (1956).
4 C. B. Reilly and M. Orchin. American Chemical Society Meeting. Atlantic City. September (1956).
5 W. Neumann, P. J. Holtschmidt and H. Kallert. Fourth Rubber Technology Conference, London, **4**, 738 (1962).
6 S. H. Metzger, Jr. and J. M. Cross, *American Chem. Soc. Div. Polm. Chem.* Atlantic Ciry, September (1968), No. 2, 1572.
7 S. W. Lasoski, Jr. and W. H. Cobbs, Jr., *J. Polm. Sci.* **36**, 21 (1959).
8 R. C. Golike and S. W. Lasoski, *J. Physical Chem.* **64**, 895 -898 (1960).
9 O. Bayer, Angew. Chem. A59. 257 (1947).
10 D. Pettit, *J. Soc. Leather Trade Chemists.* **45**, 415 (1961).
11 Kuno. 'Human Perspiration'. Published by: Thomas (U.S.A.).
12 G. Ball, *Rubber Journal.* **147**, No. 1, 30 -33 (1965).
13 SATRA Flexing Test. STM. 101.
14 H. Leaderman, 'Elastic and Creep Properties of Filamentous Materials'. The Textile Foundation. Washington (1943).
15 J. D. Ferry, 'Viscoelastic Properties of Polymers', John Wiley & Sons Inc., New York (1961).
16 R. W. Hefty, *Modern Plastics.* Technical Section. **43**, No. 8, 163-168 (1966).
17 S. Glasstone, 'Textbook of Physical Chemistry', Macmillan. 2nd Edn. (1946).
18 A. T. James and V. R. Wheatley, *Biochem. J.* **63**, 269 (1956).
19 R. M. B. Mackenna, V. R. Wheatley and A. Wormall, *Biochem. J.* **52**, 161 (1952).

CHAPTER 7

Durability of poromeric materials in wear

J. C. BISSON

INTRODUCTION

FOUR of the most important claims made by manufacturers of poromerics relate to durability in wear. They are that shoes having poromeric uppers retain their new appearance throughout the life of the shoe, they can be cleaned much more easily than shoes with leather uppers, are highly scuff resistant and are not prone to flex cracking in wear. In this paper it is hoped to consider these claims of durability in wear objectively, relate wear trial data and test results to material structure, and illustrate how the shoe manufacturer can influence quite markedly the durability of shoes with poromeric uppers by the correct choice of components and by giving due attention to detail in the factory.

WEAR TRIALS

In discussing the durability of poromerics let us first consider what happens to shoes in wear. They are worn by tall, thin people and short, fat people, by people who squeeze their feet into shoes which are too small, by people with unusual types of gait, by people who trip up over kerbstones, by people who crawl round on the floor after children and by normal people. Unfortunately for the footwear industry, but fortunately for humanity there appear to be very few normal people! Similarly there are considerable differences in the number of hours for which shoes are worn in a day, the number of miles which are walked in a day and the weather conditions prevailing at the time of wear. Despite problems of using so fickle and unreliable an instrument as woman, or for that matter man, when compared with the precise engineering tolerances of flexing jaws, the wear trial must be the primary standard for assessing durability in wear, and test machines at best can only be secondary standards.

The wear trial is, therefore, of paramount importance and it is essential to carry out statistically planned wear trials to ensure that the results at the end of the trial are meaningful. The SATRA article by J. R. Manning entitled 'The Design of Field Trials for Footwear' is very valuable in this context.

From what I have said already it is obviously necessary to have several wearers in any wear trial to allow for differences in fit and conditions of wear. Let us now briefly consider the statistics involved in carrying out a simple wear trial to differentiate between poromerics A and B. As an initial premise we will assume that both materials are equal and will use the wear trial to disprove this thesis. If both materials are equal and we have just one wearer there is a 50–50 chance that poromeric A will be preferred. With two wearers there is a one in four chance that both will prefer poromeric A. The chance of a unanimous preference for poromeric A reduces to one in eight with three wearers, one in sixteen with four wearers and one in thirty-two with five wearers.

Therefore, in a trial with five wearers, it is rather unlikely that all will prefer poromeric A if A is equal to B and hence we can conclude, with only a small risk, that poromeric A truly is superior to poromeric B. Thus, five wearers is an absolute minimum for drawing a conclusion that poromeric A is superior to poromeric B with at least 95% confidence, even when the preferences are unanimous. 95% confidence means that there is a one in twenty chance that you will draw the wrong conclusion. Obviously if you travel by aeroplane you ought to have far more than 95% confidence that it will land without crashing. The greater the confidence required the more expensive it is to carry out tests to prove it and 95% confidence seems to be a reasonable compromise for shoe wear trials, between the certainty of the answer and the cost of the trial.

Table 7.1. Table showing the number of preferences which can be tolerated for poromeric B, whilst still retaining 95% confidence that poromeric A is superior to poromeric B, for different sizes of wear trial.

Number of wearers	Prefer A	Prefer B
5	5	0
6	5	1
7	6	1
8	7	1
9	7	2
10	8	2
11	9	2
12	9	3

From Table 7.1 it can be seen that with between six and eight wearers there is 95% confidence that poromeric A is superior to poromeric B if one wearer prefers poromeric B. When there are between nine and eleven wearers two can prefer poromeric B, and with twelve wearers three can prefer poromeric B, whilst there is still 95% confidence that poromeric A is superior to poromeric B. It is clear, therefore, that the results obtained from wear trials containing less than twelve wearers are unlikely to be very conclusive and the dangers of basing one's marketing policy on what the office girl says are considerable.

Wear trials are tedious, expensive and take a long time to complete, yet they are essential in the footwear industry which depends so much

PLATE 11

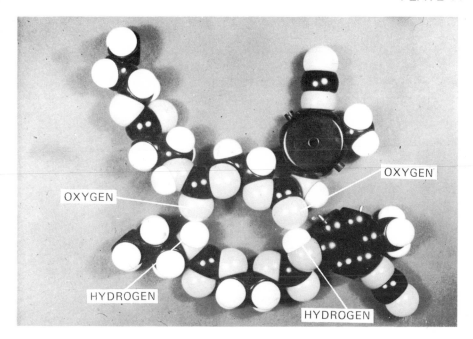

Fig. 6.4. Molecular model illustrating ease of formation of hydrogen bonds between polyurethane chains.

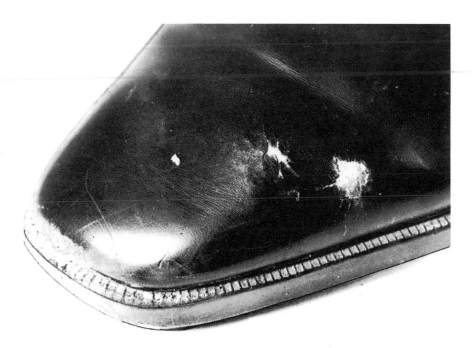

Fig. 6.6. Poromeric shoe showing damaged area in close-up.

PLATE 12

Fig. 6.8. Photomicrograph of a cross-section of poromeric B degraded in the laboratory in steam at 120°C for 12 hours. In this case cracks are present on the surface skin (grain).

Fig. 6.7. Photomicrograph of a cross-section of poromeric B taken from a worn shoe similar to Fig. 6.6, showing cracks close to the microporous layer–substrate junction. (The microporous layer is the wide black and narrow white bands on the left of the picture.)

PLATE 13

Fig. 6.9. Sample of poromeric B repeatedly extended by a ¾-inch hemisphere after hydrolysis for 12 hours at 120°C. Sample was extended 600 times at a rate of one extension per second.

VAMP FLEX SAMPLE
(1 million flexes)

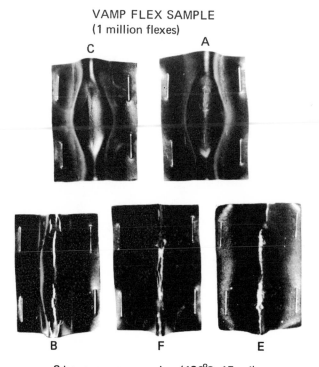

8 hours pressure cooker (120°C, 15 psi)

Fig. 6.11. Effects of steam (120°C) hydrolysis on five poromeric materials. The samples were hydrolysed at 120°C for 8 hours, reconditioned for 48 hours at 65% R.H./20°C and then flexed for 1 million flexes on the SATRA flexing machine (STM. 101).

PLATE 14

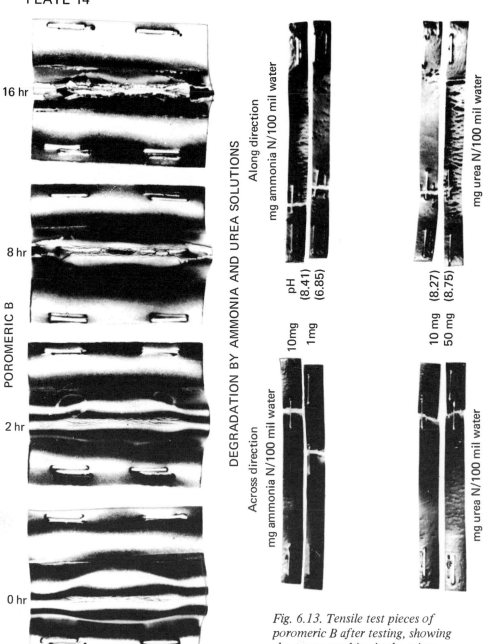

POROMERIC B

16 hr

8 hr

2 hr

0 hr

DEGRADATION BY AMMONIA AND UREA SOLUTIONS

Along direction
mg ammonia N/100 mil water

Across direction
mg ammonia N/100 mil water

pH
10mg (8.41)
1mg (6.85)

mg urea N/100 mil water

10 mg (8.27)
50 mg (8.75)

mg urea N/100 mil water

Fig. 6.12. The effect of steam
(120°C) hydrolysis on one
poromeric for different exposure
times. After hydrolysis and
reconditioning the samples were
flexed 1 million times on the
SATRA flexing machine
(STM. 101).

Fig. 6.13. Tensile test pieces of
poromeric B after testing, showing
the severe cracking in the microporous layer due to loss of elastic
properties as a result of hydrolysis
in very dilute solutions of ammonia
and urea. The ammonia and urea
concentrations were comparable
with those present in sweat.

PLATE 15

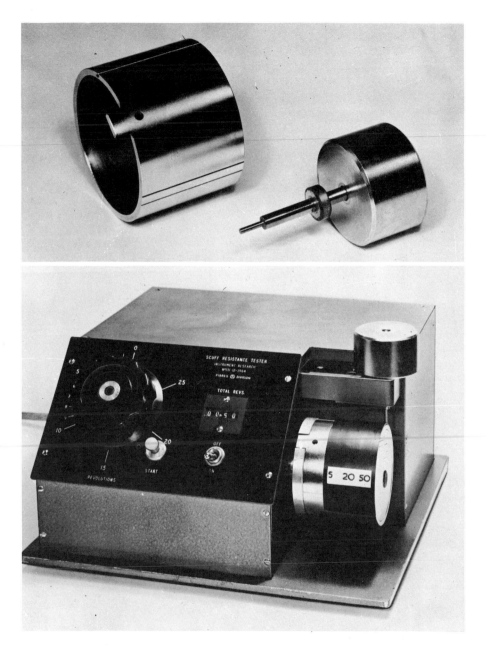

Fig. 7.5. ICI Scuff Tester (Insert showing sleeve on which the specimen is mounted, and the scuffing tool).

PLATE 16

Fig. 7.6. Abrasion Tester (inset showing emery cloth and specimen holders).

PLATE 17

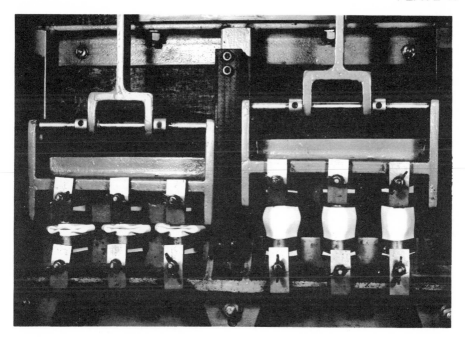

Fig. 7.7. SATRA Vamp Flex Machine.

Fig. 7.8. Balley Flexometer.

PLATE 18

Fig. 7.9. Newark Flex Tester.

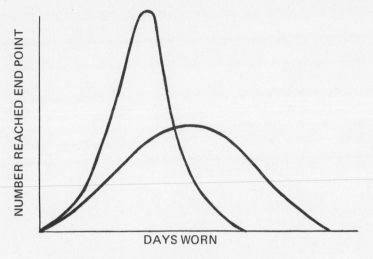

Fig. 7.1. Two normal distribution curves.

on new styles and new materials. One of the most frequent objectives of wear trials is to estimate the percentage of shoes showing failure after a given wear period. The time taken to carry out a wear trial of this type can be considerably reduced if there is information as to the expected distribution of wear lives. Analysis of our own wear trial data has shown that in many cases the wear lives approximate to a normal distribution. It is virtually impossible to extrapolate a normal distribution curve (Fig. 7.1.) from its tail, to estimate the failures after a longer wear period. However, it is quite simple to transform a cumulative normal distribution into a straight line by plotting the days worn

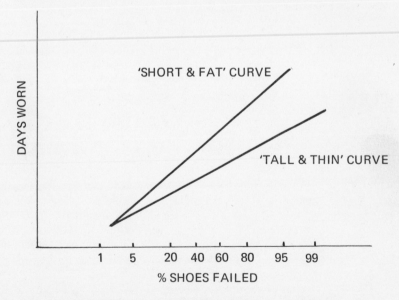

Fig. 7.2. Conversion of normal distribution curves into straight lines, by plotting on arithmetic 'probability' paper.

against the cumulative percentage of failures on 'arithmetic probability' paper (Fig. 7.2). A cumulative percentage plot is known as an ogive, and if a normal distribution can be assumed, the ogive can be extrapolated to get an estimate of the failures after a longer wear period.

A further reduction in the time taken to carry out a wear trial can be achieved by using a novel analytical technique developed by our statisticians. This technique takes account of the wear periods of shoes which have *not* failed as well as the wear lives of shoes which have failed, and can probably best be illustrated by means of an example. The data obtained from two hypothetical wear trials, each containing 100 shoes, are shown in Table 7.2. In each trial 12 shoes have failed and using only the wear lives of the shoes which have failed, the ogive stops after 12% failures in each case and one would conclude that the trials had given the same results. This is not so, and by taking account of the wear periods of the shoes which have not failed, it is possible to predict accurately up to the 25% failure stage in trial A and up to the 17% failure stage in trial B without making any assumptions as to the distribution of the wear lives (Fig. 7.3).

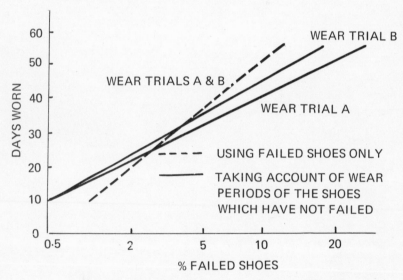

Fig. 7.3. *Wear life ogives for two hypothetical wear trials.*

If we now move from the hypothetical example to an actual wear trial the saving in time can be illustrated quite easily. One hundred and fifty pairs of shoes were issued to wearers in the spring of 1966 in order to assess how rapidly a certain type of failure became apparent in the shoes. Following an inspection on August 12, 1966, when only 8% of the shoes had reached the end point the statisticians were able to predict accurately the wear life ogive to the 20% failure stage, by taking account of the wear periods of the shoes which had not failed (Fig. 7.4). Based on experience of earlier wear trials in which the wear life ogives approximated to straight lines we extrapolated this ogive to

Table 7.2. Data from two hypothetical wear trials

Wear Trial A		Wear Trial B	
Wear failures 12		Wear failures 12	
Still in wear 88		Still in wear 88	
Wear lives for failed shoes	Wear periods for shoes still in wear	Wear lives for failed shoes	Wear periods for shoes still in wear
10 18 27 32 38	2 3 5 5 6	10 18 27 32 38	5 8 12 14 16
40 43 45 49 52	8 8 8 9 12	40 43 45 49 52	17 19 20 20 22
52 55	13 13 15 16 16	52 55	24 24 26 26 30
	16 17 17 18 18		32 34 36 37 38
	20 21 22 24 25		39 39 40 41 42
	25 28 28 30 31		42 42 42 43 44
	31 32 33 33 33		44 44 45 45 45
	34 35 35 37 38		46 47 47 48 48
	39 39 40 41 42		49 50 50 50 51
	42 42 42 43 44		52 53 54 54 55
	44 44 45 45 45		55 56 57 58 59
	46 47 47 48 48		60 60 60 60 61
	49 50 50 50 51		62 62 63 63 64
	52 53 54 54 55		64 65 65 65 65
	55 56 57 58 59		66 66 67 68 69
	60 60 60 60 61		70 70 70 72 72
	62 63 63 64 64		74 75 75 77 79
	64 65 65		80 82 84

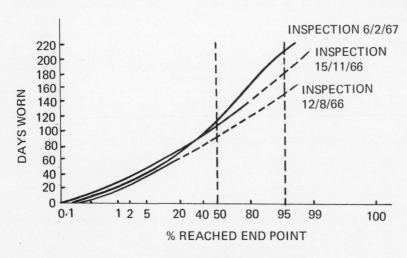

Fig. 7.4. MK VI wear trial.

get an estimate of the time taken to reach the 50 percentile and the 80 percentile (dotted line). The shoes were then worn for a further six months and the actual ogives plotted. These showed that when only 8% of the shoes had reached the end point the wear life for the 50 percentile was predicted to within 12 days of the actual wear life and that for the 80 percentile to within 40 days of the actual wear life.

The accuracy of these predictions was not perfect, but at least the predicted wear lives were of the right order and we were immediately able to act on the information that the wear life of the 50 percentile was about 100 days without having to wait a further two months for this wear period to be reached.

LABORATORY TESTS

Wear trials show that poromerics are not a group of almost identical products in terms of durability in wear. Indeed it would be highly surprising if they were when one considers the difference in raw materials and structural design. These products have all evolved as a result of a series of compromises between aesthetic appeal, foot comfort requirements, ease of shoe manufacture and durability in wear. Unfortunately these properties frequently oppose one another; greater durability may be obtained at the expense of foot comfort, improvements in the ease of shoe manufacture may involve a reduction in the aesthetic appeal of the product. Not surprisingly manufacturers of poromerics differ in their opinions as to the relative importance of these properties. In fact each manufacturer normally modifies the balance when moving from a product suitable for men's shoes to one suitable for ladies' shoes.

What is important is that the material should perform adequately in the type of footwear in which it is used. Standards are not absolute; a poromeric which would be completely unsatisfactory in injection moulded shoes may be perfectly suitable for ladies' fashion shoes and the converse could equally be true for entirely different reasons. In designing a test machine the objective is to get a rapid method of assessment of a particular property which correlates with wear. Wear trials are relatively expensive and tedious to carry out, with the result that test rigs tend to accumulate in development laboratories and, by virtue of their fascinating action and long period of use, assume an importance which is quite unjustified in terms of predicting durability in wear.

Retention of new shoe appearance throughout the life of the shoe is a common claim and covers such properties as shape retention, break, effect of cleaning, scuff and abrasion resistance. Undoubtedly the claim that poromerics are superior to leather in this respect is supported by wear trial evidence, but there are nevertheless significant differences between the various poromerics.

The traditional assessment of break in leather by compressing the grain layer in the fingers using a rolling action, gives a good indication of the break pattern to be expected in the shoes. A more controlled test is to cycle the material for five minutes on the SATRA vamp flex machine before examination of the break pattern. Fineness of break normally depends on the position of the neutral axis of bending in the material coupled with the modulus gradient within the structure.

Scuff and abrasion resistance depend on the chemical structure of the polyurethane coating, on the way in which the final coating layer is applied and on the physical nature of the layer. Solid films are more difficult to rupture than discontinuous layers and in general the more thermoplastic the coating the poorer its scuff resistance. Numerous types of scuffing and abrasive actions take place in wear and it is just not possible to reproduce all these actions in the laboratory. Our efforts to devise a single test which correlates with wear have been unsuccessful, but by using two machines with totally different actions it is possible to predict quite accurately the scuff and abrasion resistance of materials in wear. The scuff tester, Fig. 7.5, which was designed by our instrument engineers, consists of a driven metal roll mounted off centre on the drive shaft. The specimen to be tested is mounted on a sleeve which is positioned on the roll by means of a locating tongue and held securely by a spring-loaded ball bearing. The roll rotates at a fixed speed of 25 revolutions per minute and a pre-selector control is fitted to enable a specific number of revolutions to be carried out. The scuffing tool is a hardened steel spindle with a tungsten carbide tip. It is mounted in a rotating ball bush and retained in the bush by a collar. The ball bush is mounted vertically, off centre from the drive shaft, and the tool is loaded to a total weight of 500 grammes. As the sleeve rotates, the specimen is struck by the tip of the tool and contact with the specimen is maintained through 60° of arc. This test gives a very good indication of the damage likely to be caused in wear by a sharp blow, such as tripping over a kerbstone or less violently by repeatedly striking one heel against the other whilst walking.

The second test involves abrading the specimen against Grade 'O' emery cloth (Fig. 7.6). The apparatus was originally designed for abrading carpets by the Wool Industries Research Association. A circular specimen is mounted in a holder which is driven by a shaft in contact with a rotating disc of emery cloth. The specimen is examined after 10 revolutions, the type of abrasion recorded and the area not abraded measured. This is a particularly severe test but it correlates well with the general abrasion damage observed in a shoe after an extended period of wear. It also provides a useful sample for assessing how easily the abrasion damage likely to occur in wear can be covered up using wax polishes. It is worth commenting that the type of removal and ease of repairing the damage are more important in predicting appearance in wear than the actual area abraded.

Ease of cleaning depends very largely on what has to be removed and covered up. All poromerics will withstand water, and a damp cloth, with or without detergent, will remove normal dirt and most common stains. However, this is far from saying that all poromeric shoes retain a satisfactory appearance when cleaned in this way. The surface is frequently difficult to wet out with water and this can lead to patchiness on drying and the lustre frequently leaves something to be desired.

Our wear trial experience is that it was not just the Führer's army who clicked their heels, and one of the main problems is covering up minor scuffs particularly on the inside of the heels. In my comments on scuff resistance I mentioned that discontinuous layers could be scuffed more

107

easily than solid films. Discontinuous layers having poor adhesion can be scuffed extremely easily and spraying poromeric shoes with a conventional shoe dressing in the finishing department leads to a discontinuous layer having abysmally poor adhesion. Considerable advances have been made in improving the adhesion of shoe finishes designed specifically for poromerics and many of these produce very pleasing effects. However, my own view is that many poromerics require an occasional wax polish to cover up minor scuff marks and restore the lustre of the upper and that, where shoe finishes are put on in the factory, occasional polishing becomes essential. Claims of easy maintenance compared with leather are fully justified, but for the more discriminating wearer an occasional wax polish is probably necessary for most poromerics.

The claim that poromerics are not prone to cracking in wear, as a result of mechanical flexing, is, in general, true. Analysis of high-speed films taken of shoes in wear shows that there are major differences in the flexing patterns of poromerics depending upon the structure of the materials. In addition the differences in crease pattern between wearers are very considerable and there is also the interaction of chemical effects caused, either directly or indirectly, by perspiration. Chemical degradation is the subject of a separate paper (Chapter 6) and here I am concerned solely with the effects of mechanical flexing. To simulate all the mechanical flexing actions which take place in wear is clearly impossible. At least three types of machine with different flexing actions are in common use and each can claim to correlate with certain aspects of wear performance.

The SATRA vamp flex machine (Fig. 7.7) is undoubtedly the best known in this country and reproduces well the type of crease pattern which occurs in the centre of the vamp. It is commonly stated that one million cycles on this machine prior to failure represents an acceptable wear performance. This is perhaps a rather too general conclusion to draw as other types of flexing action are also important in wear, but it certainly gives a valuable indication of wear performance.

The Bally Flexometer (Fig. 7.8) uses a rolling action in which the specimen is subjected to severe shear forces. It is less obvious whether any wear pattern is being simulated in this test, but it gives a reliable indication of whether any delamination failures can be expected in wear, which would not normally be shown up on the SATRA machine.

Some authorities maintain that there is an eight to one or ten to one speed advantage using the Bally machine compared with the SATRA machine. I prefer to think of them as two machines having quite different flexing actions which show up totally different types of failure, both of which are important in wear.

The Newark flex tester (Fig. 7.9) is an American machine in which the specimen is clamped in the form of a cylinder, which is then compressed. The length of the cylinder should be proportional to the thickness of the material, and it is claimed that this enables direct comparisons to be made between materials of different substance. Because the same settings for different substance materials are used on the SATRA and Bally machines it is impossible to draw direct comparisons between different poromerics as the extension and compression cycles are influenced quite markedly by the substance of the material in a way which does not reflect what happens in wear.

Cold flex testing is also important in assessing durability in wear as all poromerics show a fall-off in flexing performance as the temperature is reduced. There is normally a critical temperature below which the flexing performance is very poor which depends on the nature of the coating, and it is, therefore, important to ensure that the critical temperature is not above the lowest temperature likely to be encountered in wear. One word of warning is necessary here: when a poromeric is flexed at 300 or more cycles per minute the work done causes a significant rise in temperature of the specimen. It is, therefore, essential to check the actual temperature of the material as this could easily be 10 or more degrees higher that that of the surroundings.

CONTRIBUTION OF THE SHOE MANUFACTURER

It is a very fair question to ask why there are more restrictions in the shoe factory when using poromerics than when using leather. The simple answer to this is that for most types of shoes the tensile properties of upper leathers are, in engineering terms, considerably overbuilt. The poromerics are offering additional properties, such as easy care and retention of new appearance but at the same time the safety margins associated with some properties are significantly reduced. For example, the tear strengths of poromerics are normally between half and two-thirds those of leathers of similar substance. The parts of a shoe most vulnerable to tearing in wear are those where the upper has been reduced in substance. In Fig. 7.10 one can see how the tear strengths of leather and a number of poromerics are affected as the substance is reduced. The rate at which the tear strength of a poromeric falls off as the substance is reduced is highly dependent on the material structure,

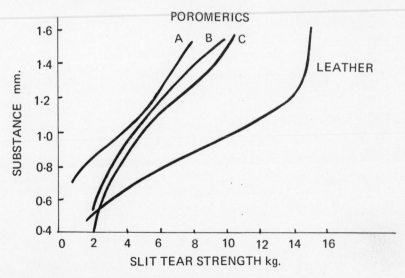

Fig. 7.10. Graphs showing the relationship between tear strength and substance for leather and three poromerics.

in particular the types and degree of consolidation of the fibres in the substrate, whether there is a fabric interlayer, and thickness of the coating. It can be seen that the tear strength of the full substance material does not necessarily indicate the tendency of a seam to tear in wear.

Tapes and lining materials play a significant part in ensuring that poromeric shoes are able to withstand the conditions of wear and must be selected to complement the load/extension curve of the poromeric. In Fig. 7.11 the load/extension curve of Ortix is plotted alongside load/extension curves for two lining materials. It can be seen that if the stiff cotton lining were used there would be very little load sharing between the lining and the Ortix in the working area and this could easily lead to premature rupture of the lining followed by complete transfer of the load to the Ortix with subsequent failure. With the faille lining on the other hand, the load/extension curves complement each other and this would lead to substantial load sharing in the working area, which would make the shoe much more resistant to breakdown in wear.

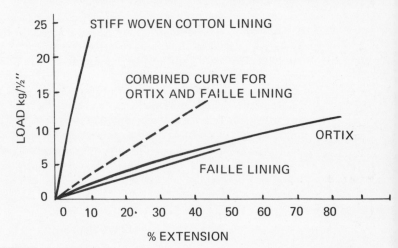

Fig. 7.11. Load/extension curves for Ortix and two typical linings.

To be fully effective reinforcing tapes should be inserted in toplines without overfeeding. Most skived poromerics can be stretched fairly easily and, unless the foot on the folding machine is set to avoid drag on the material, it is quite easy to stretch the poromeric and overfeed the tape. The effect of this can be seen in Fig. 7.12. To have 3% overfeed of the tape on the poromeric, which can be obtained quite easily, means that until the poromeric has stretched 3% there is no reinforcing action on the part of the tape and, although this is unlikely to lead to failure in the shoe, the retention of new-shoe looks will be lost as it will result in a baggy and uneven topline.

CONCLUSION

In conclusion I would like to summarize the main points in this paper. The primary standard for any assessment of durability is the wear trial, which must be carried out on a sufficiently large scale to be meaningful.

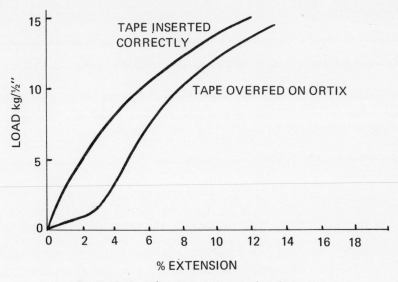

Fig. 7.12. Load/extension curves of toplines.

Laboratory tests are much cheaper and quicker to carry out, but are worthless unless they relate to wear experience.

Wear trials indicate that in general poromerics live up to the durability claims made for them. Where there are differences between products these can normally be related to the material structure and arise from the fact that each poromeric is a different compromise between a number of conflicting requirements.

Although such properties as scuff resistance and flexing performance are built in by the poromeric manufacturer, the shoe manufacturer can influence quite markedly the overall durability of poromeric shoes in wear by his choice of components and by paying due attention to detail in the factory.

111

CHAPTER 8

Purchasing and economics of poromerics

G. DRACUP

THE objectives of the industrial buyer are in the long term to ensure an adequate supply of raw materials for the product and in the short term to select from the materials currently available those best suited for the intended purpose. The main factors which he must take into account are:

1 technical properties
2 aesthetic characteristics
3 price
4 availability

These factors are not in any strict order of priority since the emphasis will vary from one situation to another. For the purposes of this paper it has been assumed that the technical and aesthetic requirements of the shoe industry can be satisfied by the poromeric materials.

Let us consider first the question of availability since it appears that an anticipated shortage in the supply of hides and skins provides the basic incentive for companies to develop man-made alternatives. Studies have been carried out which suggest that in the 1980s the supply of hides and skins will frustrate the demand for leather by about 30%. The props of this argument are:

1 the projected rise in the human population
2 the rise in the standard of living of the world population

There are other factors which will also exert an important influence on the situation, sufficient in fact for an American student of the problem to have stated that no computer in the USA was large enough to be capable of taking them all into account.

Those of us who look forward to being involved in the shoe industry of the 1980s should therefore be encouraged by the interest being shown by the many companies investing large sums of money in the development of poromerics. We should be happy to think that we shall have leather + coated fabrics + fabrics + paper even and poromerics too. With all of these at our disposal there seems to be little danger of being handicapped by a shortage of shoemaking material. In fact a recent statement by the Food and Agriculture Organization of the United Nations Organization suggests that the animal population is losing less ground than anticipated and there seems to be some confirmation of the argument that rising living standards will bring about an increase in meat consumption and therefore an increase in the supply of hides and skins.

But assuming that poromerics will establish themselves as the first alternative to leather, what is the outlook? Reference is often made to the example of the textile industry and the impact of man-made fibres on it. If we consider wool which, as a natural product, is similar in many ways to leather, we see that consumption has risen since the war by 50%. This in no way suggests that man-made fibres have not had a very marked effect on the wool trade. They have indeed established themselves very firmly in the market, but since 1961 the wool growers have put up very stiff resistance, and very effectively too, and their example will no doubt spur on the leather industry to preserve its pride of place in the shoe industry and to enjoy its share of the increasing market.

A very significant factor in the penetration of synthetic fibres in the textile industry has of course been that of price. Huge investments have had to be made in the development of the products and the provision of production capacity, and in addition to this very substantial promotion programmes have been necessary to make the consumer aware of the new products and to persuade him or her to purchase them. Once these battles have been won then the competition begins in earnest and the synthetic product has shown a consistent downward trend in price. This has been a distinct advantage, especially since the natural product tends to be so unstable in price that the buyer can never be very confident in predicting future costs even in the relatively short term.

While this is an important factor it does not, however, state the whole case as far as price and spending habits are concerned. In the UK for instance the knitwear industry can sell wool to the consumer at a premium of 40% over the synthetic fibre and in the worsted suiting trade wool can command a 60% premium. In the USA where synthetic materials might be regarded as more readily acceptable, the differences are even greater (50% and 100% respectively). And remember that against this background of disparity in price, wool consumption has risen by 50% since the war and is still increasing slowly.

It should also be remembered before drawing any conclusions from the development of the synthetic fibres industry that the natural fibres are not by-products of another commodity in the same way as hides and skins are. How many instances are there of animals being reared for their skins alone? On the other hand, how many skins never reach the tanner simply because their low value does not under present circumstances justify their collection? If hides and skins produced by the meat industry were not tanned into leather, consider the possibilities. The least attractive of these would be the prospect of disposing of them as waste. The cost of removing what could be a serious social nuisance would not be small, although this could be recovered by increasing the price of meat. We could, of course, deal with all hides and skins as we in this country dispose of pigskins, by selling them to the housewife on the weekend joint.

There are, of course, possibilities of other uses for hides and skins and these are being developed slowly. For example, the extraction of protein for concentrated feedstuffs, sausage skins, etc, but it seems that these are not yet economically viable propositions and in any case it is doubtful whether they would be able to consume any significant quantity of the hides and skins produced. There is also of course the possibility of using the collagen fibre for the production of a material to compete with leather and the poromerics. Have we heard the last of this? Is it in fact the case that the natural fibre is too complex to lend itself to rationalization?

It would seem possible, therefore, that the problems presented by the very existence of hides and skins will in themselves ensure for leather a considerable place in the shoe materials market. And this will impose certain limits on the market for poromerics. This fact has already been faced by the companies producing poromerics and they seem to agree that their aim is to supplement the supply of leather. This being the case it is appropriate to consider what the relative positions of the various materials will be in the market.

We have seen that in the case of wool, the natural fibre can command a premium over the man-made alternative and it seems quite clear that this is due to a large extent to the fact that natural products enjoy a sort of status or snob value in the mind of the consumer. The synthetic materials, however, can create competition because of the downward tendency of price, which results from increasing scale of production. The maximum price benefits become available when a large measure of standardization is accepted.

All of this seems to indicate that poromerics will find their place in the lower to middle range of the footwear offering. It is of course impossible to be more specific than this, largely because our industry is caught in the dilemma of ever-increasing fashion consciousness on the one hand— which is not conducive to standardization—and the desire to rationalize its methods of production on the other hand which makes for less flexibility to meet the fashion demands of the market. Perhaps this dilemma will be removed for us by the almost inevitable forces of technological progress. Anyone who attended the BBSI Conference at Eastbourne in 1966 and heard the very competent lecture by the American engineer, Mr Walter Abel, could not fail to be impressed by the picture he painted of the possibilities for future developments in the shoe industry. Perhaps we may be justified in doubting whether the industry can be adapted to make use of some of the ideas he put forward and it could be argued that we have yet to see a shoemaking material with the qualities necessary to enable us to achieve his dream. One thing is certain, however, namely that his view of the future involves a new generation of equipment, which will mean a heavy programme of capital investment in the industry. Unless leather proves to be capable of greater rationalization, it may be left behind, assuming, of course, that we can afford to do without what has so far been an extremely valuable commodity.

But what is the position now? Using the equipment and methods which are today conventional in our industry, what are the relative positions of leather and poromerics and other upper materials?

So far the use of poromerics has been confined to shoes in the middle to upper prices ranges. This has been brought about deliberately by the marketing policy of the poromeric manufacturers, who because of the wish to establish an image of high quality have been able to fix their selling prices so that shoe manufacturers could only afford to use their material in the higher priced shoes. On the other hand, the pvc-coated cloths are found in the lower priced shoes. Here there is no overriding pricing strategy in this sense and straightforward costing considerations have determined the situation.

Before anyone shouts me down, let me hasten to say that patent finishes are excluded from these remarks, because these are a special case: it is true that they account for the bulk of pvc-coated fabrics used in uppers, but a very good case can be made out for using them in a wide range of shoes on the grounds of suitability for the intended purpose.

The pattern which has been established over the last two or three years of poromerics in the middle to high priced shoes and other non-leather materials in the lower price brackets becomes significant when the advantages claimed for poromerics in production economics are analysed.

By far the most important of these is the saving in area of material required for a shoe. Compared with leather, poromerics can be cut with savings in area varying from 10-25%. The range of the saving is wide because it depends on the type of shoe being cut and the quality standards being aimed at. It also depends on the type of leather with which the comparison is being made. Generally speaking, smaller skins are cut less exhaustively than side leathers, for example, and consequently the potential saving arising from economies in cutting the regularly shaped poromeric material compared with side leather will be less than when compared with calf. In other words, if you can cut 85% of a side leather (including the unavoidable pattern waste) into shoes then the maximum saving can only be the remaining 15%. This will become an increasingly important factor if my earlier comments are correct and poromerics find their main use in the lower to middle priced shoes of the volume market where side leathers are the predominant material. Of course, the poromerics have no advantage over other materials supplied in rolls as far as area savings in cutting are concerned.

Another factor to be taken into account in considering area savings is the fact that almost all roll form materials have strength-stretch characteristics of a directional nature. In general they are tighter along the roll than across the width and while this may be tolerable from the point of view of lasting it imposes a certain restriction on the cutter and can result in a slight loss to be offset against the area saving.

The other production economies claimed for poromerics are attributed to the uniformity of the material in comparison with the variable nature of leather. These are: labour cost savings in cutting and a reduction in the cutting skill required, simplication of manufacturing operations by the reduction in machine adjustments often found necessary to cope with the variable characteristics of leather, and a reduction in the finishing operations necessary. Of course it is impossible to profit from these benefits of material uniformity unless the scale of usage is sufficient to set up separate production lines to handle these materials. In fact to mix leather and poromerics on a production line can cause serious headaches for supervisors. There are of course many advantages to be gained from specialization and mass production techniques whatever the material being used, but it is to be expected that materials of uniform characteristics lend themselves better to these techniques than does leather.

We are a long way yet from Mr Abel's shoe industry of the future. Whether we shall fly there on the wings of a poromeric or jog along on the back of the cow are questions which are perhaps best put to the computer when they find the one capable of the answer.

CHAPTER 9

Poromerics in the shoe factory

J. C. WADE

INTRODUCTION

WE are probably at one of the most difficult stages in poromeric technology in the shoe factory. Few manufacturers are making sufficient poromeric shoes to warrant the setting up of separate plants designed specifically to make shoes from poromerics and to obtain the full economies from them. Rather than having separate plants for leather and poromeric shoes, it is usually necessary to make the two side by side which can obviously lead to complications.

This paper is devoted to the techniques that have been developed specifically for poromeric shoes, and also to the compromises that it is desirable to make in order to make leather and poromeric shoes side by side in the same plant, in most cases on the same equipment with as little disruption as possible.

Despite the wide variations in structure and properties of the various poromerics that are commercially available, they all respond to a similar general treatment in the shoe factory with the exception of one or two operations. This simplifies matters considerably as in most cases the comments here will apply to all poromerics that are currently available. However, despite these generalizations, it is essential to establish the exact procedure and machine setting for each individual poromeric on each individual machine operation. Ideally, shoe specifications should be made specifically for poromeric shoes and the reasons for this will soon become apparent. Whilst this may seem a little frightening at first, most of the alterations are slight.

PATTERN CUTTING

The necessity for preparing patterns specifically for poromeric shoes cannot be over-emphasized as good patterns are the key to making good shoes from poromerics.

The patterns must be thoroughly tested until everyone concerned is satisfied that they are correct prior to making any bulk.

The patterns should have little or no spring and should be tightened at the feather line.

Patterns that are too large will lead to:

1 Excessive pleating which will cause difficulties at lasting and roughening (Fig. 9.1)

117

2 A tendency to over-pull to get the material down to the wood. This may result in orange peel on certain poromerics and will cause fall in after last slipping (Fig. 9.2).

Similarly patterns that are too tight will also result in over-pulling causing orange peel, a print through of toe puffs, stiffeners and reinforcing tapes, and fall in will occur. Rupture of the interlayer in products containing these, may also occur.

The pattern cutter should also take into consideration any directional tightness or stretch in the material and prepare the patterns accordingly.

LEATHER DEPARTMENT

There is a saving in labour as no grading of material is required. Handling costs are reduced to a minimum as is the process of issuing material to the clicking shop.

CUTTING

The decision as to whether to cut down the roll or across the roll depends upon several factors:

1 The 'stretch' characteristics of the poromeric, i.e. whether or not it is directional and if it is, whether or not it is necessary to take advantage of this

2 The cost difference of the footage required to cut uppers down the roll and across the roll.

It is desirable to cut down the roll when possible for the sake of economy. However, it is sometimes desirable to sacrifice some of this economy and cut across the roll. When the poromeric has more stretch in the across direction, cutting across the roll will assist in

1 blocking

2 overcoming orange peel on poromerics, which have this tendency

Table 9.1. Illustrates the saving in material that can be made compared with particular leathers

Style	Leather footage sq/ft pair	Poromeric 36 in wide		Poromeric 54 in wide	
		Down sq/ft pair	Across sq/ft pair	Down sq/ft pair	Across sq/ft pair
Ladies' full cut court	1·58	1·25	1·25	1·16	1·29
	Saving	21%	21%	26%	18%
Same shoe as above but	1·30	1·15	1·15	1·10	1·35
⅞ golosh	Saving	11%	11%	15%	Loss of 4%
Ladies' vamp and	1·77	1·58	1·72	1·72	1·97
quarter tie	Saving	11%	3%	3%	Loss of 11%
Men's vamp and quarter	2·31	2·00	2·03	1·96	2·03
tie	Saving	13%	12%	15%	12%
Same style as above	2·85	2·03	1·93	1·86	2·02
but full quarter, i.e. no backseam	Saving	29%	32%	35%	29%

PLATE 19

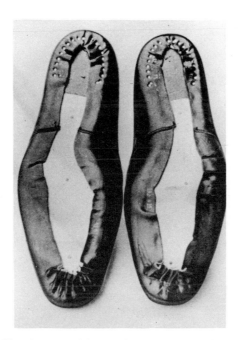

Fig. 9.1. *Pleating caused by too large a pattern. The large lasting margin can be seen. The fact that this pattern was correct on leather illustrates the necessity for preparing patterns specifically for poromeric shoes.*

Fig. 9.2. *Effects of too large a pattern on the upper, showing orange peel caused by over-pulling to get the material down to the wood.*

PLATE 20

Fig. 9.3. Embossed stitching.

PLATE 21

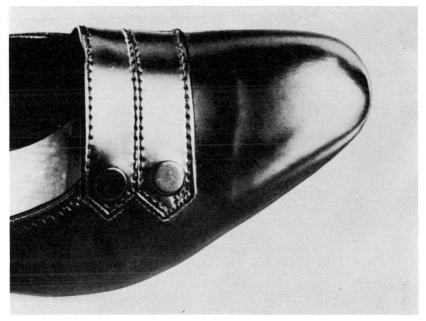

Fig. 9.4. *Print through caused by a toe puff that is too heavy in substance and is insufficiently skived.*

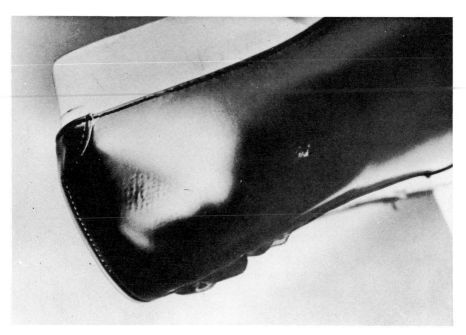

Fig. 9.5. *Heat damage caused by backpart forming (caused by using a temperature on the clamp heater of 30°C in excess of the recommended temperature). Print through from the stiffener is also evident.*

PLATE 22

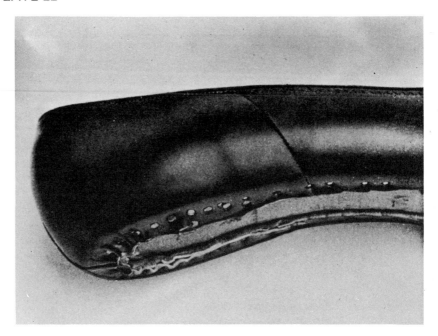

Fig. 9.6. Print through of a lining caused by over-pulling.

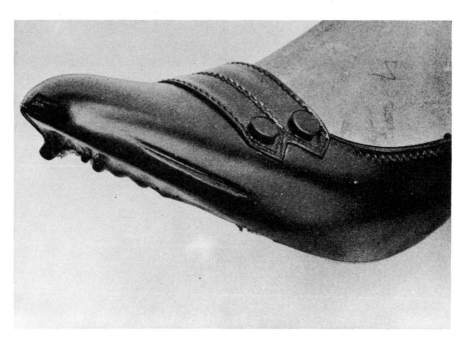

Fig. 9.7. An example of severe wiper plate damage caused by excessive heat and incorrect machine operation.

PLATE 23

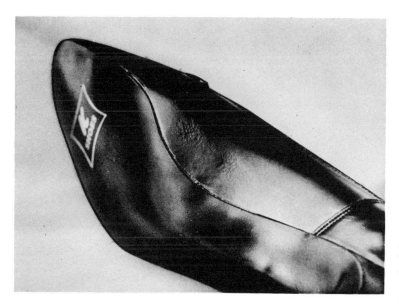

Fig. 9.9. Damage caused by using an excessively high reactivation temperature.

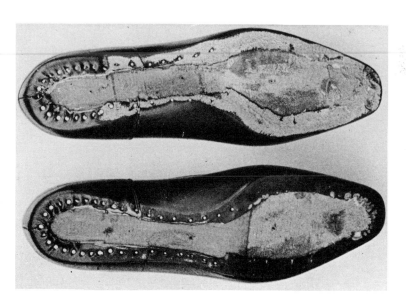

Fig. 9.8. Correct and incorrect roughing.

PLATE 24

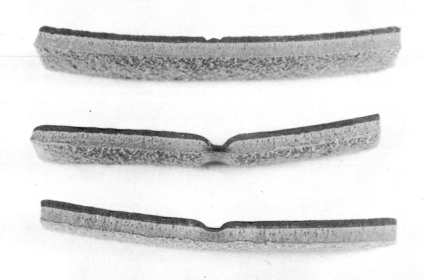

Fig. 10.1. Effect of the three embossing methods on one poromeric.
Top—*Method (a).* Centre—*Method (b).* Bottom—*Method (c).*

PLATE 25

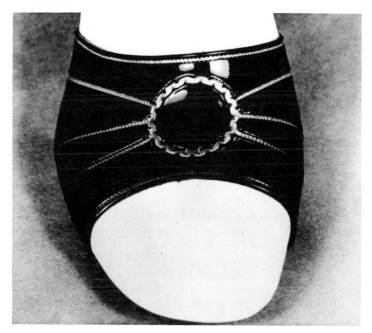

Fig. 10.2c. A typical mule with colour-embossed vamp. Colour embossing of this sort on pvc will withstand over 1 million vamp flexes.

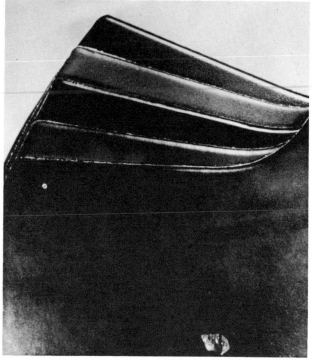

Fig. 10.3. Edges of various poromerics after HF cutting.

PLATE 26

Fig. 10.4. Compression skiving: edge-on view of pairs of parts in five poromerics—Corfam, Hi-Telac, Clarino, Ortix, PPP. The upper part of each pair is normally skived, the lower compression skived.

Corfam

Hi-Telac

Clarino

Ortix

P.P.P.

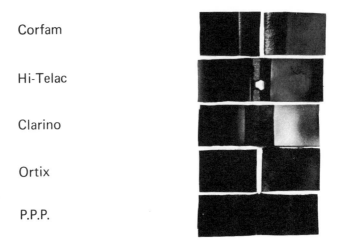

Fig. 10.5. Types of failure in peel tests.

It can be seen that the saving depends upon the following factors:

(a) the leather yield used for the comparison
(b) the particular pattern
(c) the width of the roll
(d) the direction in which the upper is cut

Full cut uppers and shoes without backseams are well worth considering giving additional savings in the closing room.

Cutting boards and knives must be in excellent condition otherwise poor edges will result. Better edges are obtained by cutting more than one layer thick.

MULTIPLE CUTTING

Cutting from the roll is considerably more economical than from ranged sheets as up to 5% is lost when the material is ranged. When it is impossible to cut from the roll, it is well worth the effort of ascertaining the best sheet size for each style.

The main problems in multiple cutting are:

1 The variations in roll widths of certain poromerics
2 Flaws or faulty material. Whilst these are fairly infrequent now and are usually tagged at the side of the roll, this is of little help when there are a number of layers at the press head
3 Fusing together of the poromeric at the edges, particularly when placed face to face. In most cases the components can be readily separated. If the fusing is severe, it has probably been caused by a blunt knife, a bad board or a material with an excessively thermoplastic finish.

Fusing can be eliminated by placing paper or polyurethane between layers. Another method is to cool the material to 0-2°C just prior to cutting.

On this method, the temperature to which a poromeric is cooled is critical in order to eliminate fusing without reaching a temperature at which the material becomes rigid. However, it is hoped that such methods do not prove to be necessary.

The saving in labour cost in the clicking shop is the main large labour cost saving that is readily apparent. Although the actual saving will obviously vary in different factories, it provides a definite advantage against leather, particularly when multiple cutting.

SKIVING DEPARTMENT

STITCHMARKING

The tendency of poromerics to curl may cause some difficulty when the cut component is placed in a template for stitchmarking or perforating. Clips should be incorporated in the template to hold the material flat.

SKIVING

There is a tendency for materials to drag. This can be minimized by covering the presser foot with ptfe tape. Alternatively the whole presser foot can be machined out of ptfe.

As a general rule, no skive should penetrate as far as the microporous layer, or as far as the interlayer in cases where this is incorporated in the material. In other words the skive must leave part of the substrate intact.

SPLITTING

As in skiving, it is essential to leave part of the substrate intact, and it is therefore inadvisable to split below 0·5 mm to 0·6 mm depending upon the poromeric concerned. It is advisable to oil lightly the surface of the material to aid feeding through the machine.

BLOCKING

The vamps should be cut 'stretch toe to heel' to minimize distortion and to aid shape retention. The vamp should be placed in the machine, grain side up. Whilst the conditions vary for different materials, the following settings give good results on Clarino:

Dwell	7 seconds
Centre blade temperature	80°C
Side plate temperature	130°C
Side plate pressure	80 psi

Blocking on men's vamps and quarter styles gives good results at lasting with the minimum lasting strains, and aids shape retention considerably. The process is therefore particularly valuable when it is impossible to use the optimum heat setting conditions.

EMBOSSING (LOUIS FREEMAN MACHINE)

Some very attractive results can easily be obtained with this technique (Fig. 9.3).

The critical factors are the temperature, pressure and dwell. Obviously the temperature varies according to the poromeric being processed; 121°C (250°F) on the embossing plate is a good starting point. The pressure should fall between the setting of 0 and 15. There is no dwell time

CLOSING

BACKSEAMS

Rubbing down achieves little other than a tendency to cause burst backseams. This operation should be omitted. The seams should be seam reduced, taped and conformed.

THERMO-BONDING OF LININGS BY PRESS

It is essential that the table and press head are kept smooth and clean, otherwise marks will be embossed into the surface of the material.

Temperatures must be reduced to prevent damage to the material. It therefore follows that the adhesive film on the lining must have a relatively low melting point in order to obtain good lamination.

For laminating sheen linings, a 3-second dwell at 110°C is a good starting point. For foam sheen this temperature can be increased, depending upon the substance of the foam, up to 160°C to compensate for the heat loss in the foam.

STITCHING

Narrow wedge needles are recommended for most normal operations. Feed wheels should not be heavily indented and it is sometimes advisable to reduce the pressure to avoid marking the material.

BEADING

This is more difficult than with leather. Straight runs and concave curves are as easy as with leather. The difficulty comes on convex curves. Very acute curves must be avoided at the design stage as these will not bead properly. Acute convex curves must be proved to be a factory proposition prior to making bulk. Beading, in the author's experience takes more time with poromerics as particular care is required to ensure even pleating.

It is particularly important to ensure that linings, interlinings, toe puffs, tapes and stiffeners are incorporated in the shoe in such a way that they leave a smooth line. Any distinct edges are prone to printing through poromerics in the early stages of lasting.

LASTING

TOE PUFFS

All known toe puffs can be used with poromerics. However, experiments should be made with different toe puffs to determine the best result on particular poromerics used on particular plants. Care must be taken to ensure that the toe puffs are well skived and are relatively smooth to avoid print through (Fig. 9.4).

Whilst it is possible to use solvent-activated toe puffs with poromerics the author prefers to avoid them because of the possibility of solvent damage to the material either directly from the puff or from handling.

STIFFENERS

Thermoplastic stiffeners are especially recommended for use with poromerics. In general backpart forming gives better lamination and much better seats than any other method.

If fibre stiffeners are used, lattices with a higher solids content are required.

THE ESSENTIALS OF LASTING POROMERICS

1 Avoid excessive heat
2 Ensure that all pads on machines are smooth and clean
3 Keep lasting strains to the minimum necessary to get the material down to the wood
4 Lubricate the material at points where frictional drag occurs. Never use silicones for this purpose as sole bonds may be affected
5 Use peg racks to avoid marking the material

Mulling of poromerics is not necessary.

BACKPART FORMING

If turret heating is employed, normal conditions should be satisfactory. However, on clamp heaters the temperature should be reduced otherwise the material will be damaged (see Fig. 9.5). The pincer pressure must be no more than 20–30 psi. It is imperative that pads are smooth and kept clean to prevent damage to the surface of the material. In some cases, particularly on patent finishes, it is beneficial to smear the quarters lightly with a lubricant to assist backpart forming. Relcapenetrator (Sandoz Products Ltd) is recommended for lubricating poromerics as it has the advantage of being water soluble at pH levels above 6·4 as well as being solvent soluble. It is therefore much more readily removed and therefore less likely to interfere with sole adhesion.

PULLING OVER

This should be done with the minimum of tension required to bring the material down to the wood. If it is necessary to over-pull, then the patterns should be thoroughly examined. As has already been mentioned over-pulling will only result in:

1 falling in after slipping
2 orange peel on certain poromerics
3 rupture of the interlayer, in products containing these, such that the surface layer falls in
4 print through of components such as toe puffs, backseam tapes and stiffeners (Fig. 9.6).

Again, cleanliness of pads is most important.

MICROTACKING

It is often necessary to adjust the driver to prevent the tacks from being driven too far into the material.

BED LASTING

The wiper plates should be lubricated with soap. There is a tendency on certain poromerics for the material to recover as soon as the wire is removed just prior to welting. For this reason better results can usually be obtained from an automatic machine using nylon that is left in permanently.

SEAT LASTING

This is aided by lubricating the material in the seat region to prevent drag. It is worth while having separate bands for poromeric shoes so that delicate leathers may be processed on the same machine without being stained by lubricant. The bands must be kept clean to prevent embossing.

SEAT PRESSING

This can sometimes be done to advantage. However, it is essential to reduce the temperature considerably and to have no dwell time.

TOE LASTING USING HOT MELT ADHESIVES

When first using poromerics it is advisable to reduce the temperature of the wiper plates to avoid damage to the material (Fig. 9.7). (As experience is gained it is possible to use a temperature of 71°C (160°F) which enables both leather and poromeric shoes to be processed at the same temperature without danger.)

The technique is to so position the shoe in the machine that, prior to operating the machine, there is a 5 mm gap between the shoe and the Teflon band, and a further 5 mm gap between the Teflon band and the wiper plates. On operation, the adjustments should be such that the top of the Teflon band is 2–3 mm higher than the shoe prior to the wiper plates moving in.

If the Teflon band is too close to the shoe prior to operation, it will be driven into the material on operation, leaving a dent at the toe.

If the wiper plates are moved in too soon or if the Teflon band is positioned too low, then they will permanently damage the upper. Again, it is imperative that pads are kept smooth and clean.

FOREPART LASTING USING LATEX

The normal type of latex used in this type of machine does not give very good bonds. To overcome this, the latex should be sprayed on to 12 pairs of shoes prior to placing the first shoe in the machine in order to allow the latex to partially dry. The temperature control should be turned to low.

Alternatively, neoprene adhesive may be hand applied; this gives much better results. However, combined pull toe lasters are obviously the ideal.

LASTING MACHINES (TEMPERATURE CONTROLS)

It can be seen from the notes above that accurate temperature controls are essential for poromerics. This is an aspect which must be greatly improved on lasting machinery. Very few machines incorporate thermometers, which makes accurate control difficult. Other machines have no more than a setting of high and a setting of low which gives a 93°C (200°F) difference. Such controls are obviously completely inadequate.

HEAT SETTING

This is essential, and details of this are presented in Mr Butlin's paper (Chapter 10).

POUNDING

This is detrimental to poromerics and must not be carried out. A light scouring to remove pleats should be given. Jiggering can be done at a reduced temperature with advantage in certain cases.

HOT AIR BLASTING

This is pointless on poromerics and will only result in damage to the material.

BOTTOMING

All flat lasted shoes should have pre-finished soles or be injection moulded otherwise there is the danger of damaging the material at edge trimming. The only exception to this is if a rand is cemented to the upper when trimming can be done without fear of damage.

ROUGHENING

In order to achieve the best sole bonds the object is to dull the top surface but not to penetrate into the substrate (see Fig. 9.8). For this reason it is vital that pleats are kept to a minimum and that there is a reasonable margin where there are no pleats at the beginning of the lasted margin from the featherline in the toe region, to ensure that the sole bonds are at a maximum in this area.

For this operation, a scouring machine using 24-grit paper gives perfect results. In the absence of a scouring machine, a very fine wire roughening brush should be used.

CEMENTING

Sole attachment is straightforward. However, care must be taken to ensure that the inside waists of shoes do not become too hot during reactivation as this itself may cause damage and in any event will render the material prone to impressions from the pads (see Fig. 9.9). Once again pads must be kept smooth and clean.

ROUGH ROUNDING

A smear of lubricant round the feather edge of the material is beneficial to prevent friction.

WELT WHEELING

The temperature of the wheel must be reduced to prevent damage.

HEEL TRIMMING, SCOURING AND EDGE TRIMMING

It is necessary to protect the upper against damage at these operations.
This can be done by application of a masking tape round the feather
edge. This is best applied prior to seat piecing.

SHOE ROOM

There are a number of varying views on shoe rooming. The author's
personal view is that in most cases no attempt should be made to repair
poromeric shoes.

Having been presented with a uniform material, there is no excuse for
damaging shoes. In addition, there is no repairing system available
currently that exhibits the exceptional adhesion and flexibility
necessary to stand up to the easy-clean virtues of poromerics. Even if
there were, its use should be discouraged as the mere fact that a repair
system is available causes shoemaking faults to be covered up, thereby
preventing management from analysing the faults and rectifying them at
source.

Provided all operatives are aware of the extra care required, this policy
ultimately leads to better shoes and less rejects.

On patent, if the gloss is slightly dulled, this can be easily replaced by
applying an aqueous emulsion of polydimethylsiloxane. (Releasil
Emulsion 66 from Midland Silicones Ltd is ideal.) Allow this to dry
for approximately one minute and then polish up.

For cleaning, a solvent cleaner recommended by the poromeric
manufacturer should be used. Alternatively a silicone finish which acts as a
cleaner and a polish has much to commend it, especially if this contains
a small quantity of colour thereby colouring raw edges and any open
stitch holes. This gives a high quality finish with the minimum of labour.

If a spray dressing is favoured in order to obtain a higher gloss, then
particular care must be taken to ensure that it has a very high flex
cracking resistance. It is asking a great deal to expect this type of
dressing to withstand being cleaned with a damp cloth or even a 'hose
pipe' without flex cracking showing ultimately, whereas on a leather
shoe this would not be noticed to the same extent because of the use of
polish.

However, it should be possible virtually to eliminate the shoe room in a
100% poromeric plant when manufacturers are ordering a sufficient
quantity of material to be in a position to specify the brightness they
require. This will provide a valuable cost saving.

EFFECT OF POROMERICS ON SHOE QUALITY

How often does one hear the expression 'but we can get away with
it on leather' when a restriction is imposed by the use of poromerics.
The fact that one can 'get away with it' is a credit to the versatility of
leather. However, it does mean that a large number of leather shoes are
not made under the optimum conditions for the leather concerned.
The need for exact conditions for each poromeric ensures that shoes
made from them are of the highest quality from the manufacturing

point of view. In addition, once the machines are set up, every shoe is the same, thanks to the uniformity of the material. The elimination of repairing gives shoes that are right or wrong; there is no room for borderline cases and faults are rectified at source.

Therefore the quality of shoemaking can be expected to increase on all shoes made on a plant where some poromeric shoes are made regularly.

EFFECT ON REJECTS

When a plant makes its first bulk of poromeric shoes, a fairly high reject rate is commonplace until the bugs are ironed out and the operatives become used to handling the material. After the initial bulk the reject factor can be expected to level off to a below normal factor.

Fig. 9.10 illustrates the effect of using a poromeric patent in place of a particular leather patent so far as rejects are concerned. However, if a poromeric were used in place of a calf or side leather, one would not expect the difference to be so marked.

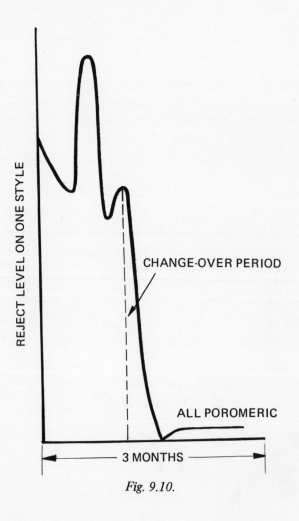

Fig. 9.10.

126

In this paper an attempt has been made to show some of the problems and means of overcoming them. It is hoped that sufficient emphasis has been made on the point that it is necessary to design shoes in poromerics from the beginning for the best results.

In conclusion, the future is going to bring many exciting developments and we must be prepared more than ever before to adapt and to alter our technology to obtain the maximum use and economy from using poromerics in the shoe factory.

CHAPTER **10**

Welding, embossing, preforming and heat setting

J. G. BUTLIN

INTRODUCTION

FOR many years shoemakers have looked forward to a 'Utopia' where an upper material is perfectly uniform in its properties, will not need stitching, can be shaped to the last with simple machines and will bond perfectly with no preparation.

Are poromerics taking us in this direction, and, if so, how far along the road have we come?

It is outside the scope of this paper to discuss whether or not these are the right properties to ask for or whether the economics of welding, preforming of simplified lasting systems are sound. However, materials which readily lend themselves to these processes will certainly be used to explore the possibilities of more economical shoemaking, and, if this exploration is successful, materials which cannot be used with the new methods could decline steadily in importance.

This paper covers the welding and embossing, heat setting and preforming properties of current poromerics and indicates some of the problems that remain to be solved. An important point is that poromerics differ widely from one another in their reaction to all these processes and few generalizations can be made about poromerics as a class.

As far as pvc upper materials are concerned the use of high-frequency heating to weld and emboss is growing rapidly. The recent introduction of double pvc-coated nylon has avoided the need to pre-laminate, and the material, if treated correctly, can give acceptable edges to the component. Excellent impressions can be made with simple embossing jigs, and developments are now in progress to 'colour emboss' uppers, thus adding a further dimension to the skill of the designer.

It is doubtful whether any poromeric will weld or emboss more readily than pvc. They will, however, be more versatile in the type of footwear that can be made (men's shoes, for example), while the absence of a woven backer and (with some) the possession of unusual compression properties, may lead to techniques which cannot be applied to leather or pvc.

EMBOSSING

Most poromerics can be embossed satisfactorily if care is taken to adjust the embossing conditions correctly for each material. How readily they

128

emboss depends to a large extent on their thermoplasticity—highly crosslinked polymers are not very thermoplastic and hence are more difficult to emboss.

Three basic embossing methods have been tried:

    (a) A simple heated die
    (b) High-frequency heating using a cold die
    (c) High-frequency heating using a heated die

The general conclusions from this work were that all three methods produce an emboss on most materials, but the quality varies with both method and material (Fig. 10.1).

Method (a). Heated-die embossing gives a well defined pattern with clear edges but with little depth of emboss. It is not possible to increase the depth of emboss by longer dwell times or higher temperatures as the surface of the material is damaged before a deep emboss is obtained. This, of course, is due to the low thermal conductivity of the poromeric material.

Method (b). High-frequency heating alone gives much greater depth of emboss (the material is heated in depth), but the edges are not quite as well defined, the time dwell needed is uneconomically long, and there is a tendency for the material to curl due to localized compression.

Method (c). The heated die plus high-frequency gives the best results; clear embossings of good depth can be obtained with very short time dwells.

With the combined use of high-frequency heating and a heated die, satisfactory embossing was achieved on Corfam, Hi-Telac, Clarino and PPP (a Porous Plastic poromeric) with a dwell time of only two seconds. Results on Ortix were not as satisfactory.

The die temperature required for optimum emboss was 90–100°C. Higher die temperatures could lead to sticking or surface marring. If high-frequency heating was used with a cold die, the dwell times required were considerably longer (3–6 seconds).

Deeply embossed patterns which are positioned on flexing areas of shoes—or areas subjected to high strains—might be imagined to lead to premature breakdown of the material or to a compressed material that is stronger than the original. To test whether such effects occurred, vamp flexing and tensile tests have been carried out on the materials listed above.

From the results of these preliminary tests it does not appear that embossing will affect the strength or wearing properties of the material.

APPLIQUÉ DECORATION

Decoration with appliqués is not as easy with poromerics as it is with pvc. To obtain a satisfactory bond between the poromeric and a pvc appliqué it appears necessary to use a polyurethane film adhesive. Wear trials have not yet been carried out to ensure that this will give adequate adhesion for difficult designs.

COLOUR EMBOSSING

PVC

POROMERIC

Fig. 10.2. Foil embossing on pvc and poromeric. (The embosses in this case were in gold and stood out very well.)

FOIL EMBOSSING

Many attractive hot stamping foils are now available and are widely used in the packaging industry for decoration, the techniques being somewhat similar to the shoe industry's well-known sock-stamping and lining-stamping operations. Whilst this type of decoration is attractive, the colour is only applied flat. When the colour is combined with embossing an inlaid effect can be produced, which is much more attractive (Fig. 10.2). This effect, i.e. colouring the valleys of the embossing, can readily be achieved, but a two-step process is needed.

The surface of the material is first stamped with the foil in the conventional manner using a heated die (80–120°C, depending on the type of foil being used) (Fig. 10.2a). The foil must then be removed and the die brought down a second time without moving the material (Fig. 10.2b). A normal embossing cycle, using high frequency, then sinks the colour into the material. Figure 10.2c shows a typical result.

A standard bar welder is probably the most suitable machine for foil embossing and an automatic foil feed can be fitted. The more costly and complicated high-frequency cutting presses could also be adapted, but only spring-loaded dies would be suitable if the foil is not to be cut through. Cutting through, leaving the cut edges coloured, would of course be possible if desired.

CUTTING AND WELDING

The use of high-frequency heating on a straight cutting operation is only of value if it can produce a pleasing edge effect. Normally it would be combined with embossing or welding to a lining material. Some poromerics will give a clear well-rounded edge when HF cut, but others suffer from the same 'whiskering' problem associated with most fabric-backed pvcs although with many poromerics this may be sufficiently slight to be acceptable (Fig. 10.3).

130

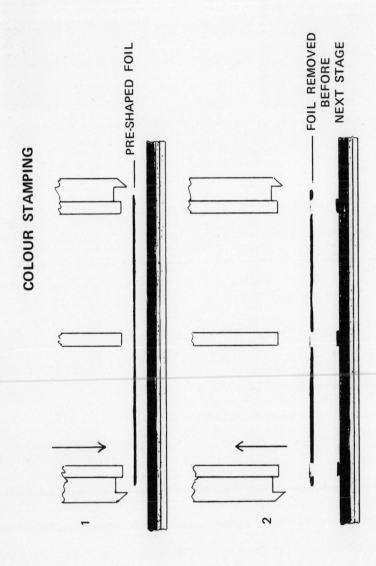

COLOUR STAMPING

PRE-SHAPED FOIL

1

2

FOIL REMOVED
BEFORE
NEXT STAGE

*Fig. 10.2a. (Colour stamping) and 10.2b. (Embossing colour) diagrams
showing stages of foil-embossing process.*

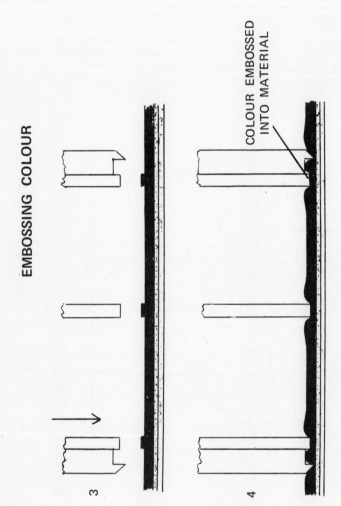

EMBOSSING COLOUR

COLOUR EMBOSSED INTO MATERIAL

Fig. 10.2b. (See also page 131.)

132

COMPRESSION SKIVING

The possibility of compression skiving poromerics (i.e. reducing the edge substance by the use of pressure and heat rather than by the removal of material) has been examined and this has given good results on some poromerics, particularly on PPP.

As Fig. 10.4 shows, the poromerics vary appreciably in their response to this treatment (it is the base material that tends to compress rather than the coating). Whether compression skiving will be economically viable is not known—the potential advantages are that cutting, skiving and lamination may possibly be combined, the edge lengths would be accurate, and the strength of the skived edge might even be greater than that of the original material in some cases.

WELDING POROMERICS

The possibility of welding poromerics without surface preparation or the use of adhesives would obviously be valuable for some applications, although whether this would lead to a complete transformation of the closing room is not yet clear.

Attempts have been made to weld both close and overlap seams, using most poromerics, and the general conclusion so far is that no material gives a sufficiently strong welded close seam, but promising results have been obtained with some materials on overlap seams.

STRENGTH OF WELDED SEAMS

Table 10.1 shows the tensile and peeling strength of various seams, both welded and stitched.

Table 10.1. Strength of seams in poromeric materials

Material	Tensile strength of various types of seam (lb/in width)				Peeling strength (lb/in width)
	Welded overlap	Welded close	Machined overlap	Machined close	Face/face weld
Corfam	NW	NW	62	61	NW
Hi-Telac	55	19	78	80	19
Clarino	38	17	40	40	16
Ortix	NW	NW	39	43	NW
PPP	53	18	42	37	9*

* Coalescence only partial, owing to incorrect welding conditions. This illustrates an important danger with welded seams.
NW = Not weldable.

Welded close seams are generally much weaker than machined close seams, as their strength depends on the strength of the coating. How well the two surfaces coalesce also influences the weld strength. Some materials will not weld at all—usually those with a high degree of crosslinking in the surface coating.

Peeling load test pieces, which are in effect wide close seams (i.e. welded over a wider area), illustrate more clearly than the normal narrow close seam the type of breakdown. Peeling loads correlate fairly well with close-seam breaking loads.

Fig. 10.5 illustrates some of the points mentioned above. Corfam and Ortix, for example, are difficult to weld. This suggests a coating of highly crosslinked polymer with low thermoplasticity. Highly crosslinked polymers are, however, usually associated with high scuff resistance and it may not be possible to obtain good weldability and very high scuff resistance.

Hi-Telac shows a breakdown very similar to that of pvc-coated fabrics; the top film breaks through and then peels from the base material.

On Clarino the surface of both members of the joint is breaking down, but it is only a shallow surface failure.

The bottom test piece illustrates one of the real dangers of welding, which is unforeseen non-coalescence of the surfaces. This is not in this case connected with the material itself (PPP, which normally welds well) but with incorrect welding conditions. This is illustrated by the difference between the breaking load of the welded close seam and the peeling load in Table 10.1. There is at present no easy way of checking the strength of a welded seam without destroying it. Similar non-coalescence effects can be produced by some types of finish that are applied to poromerics, water-resistant treatments in particular.

Reverting to Table 10.1, welded overlap seams give high breaking loads and are usually stronger than the material itself, so direct comparison is not possible.

In Fig. 10.6 the test pieces of the materials that will weld have broken remote from the seam (Hi-Telac and PPP). Clarino has broken along the line of the seam, while Corfam and Ortix have failed to join.

All the machined seams have broken along the line of stitching, and stitching has weakened some of the materials significantly. On Ortix and PPP the effect has been rather like the perforations of a postage stamp, but it is interesting to note that Clarino, Ortix and PPP have all given breaking loads of the same order. Corfam and Hi-Telac have given higher breaking loads, Hi-Telac possibly achieving the optimum conditions where both thread and material are breaking.

The following conditions were used throughout these tests:
  Welded Overlap Seam: Overlap 0·35 in; 0·5 in wide electrode.
  Welded Close Seam: Seam allowance ⅛ in; 0·04 in wide electrode.
  Machined Overlap Seam: Overlap ½ in; seam allowance ¼ in;
      16 × 4 needle. 2 oz 70s Polyfil (16.s/11) thread, top and bobbin.
  Machined Close Seam: Seam allowance ⅛ in; machine as above.
  Peel test piece: Face-to-face weld, ½ in wide electrode.

PLATE 27

Fig. 10.7. *All-welded Gibson men's shoes in PPP.*
Top—*new.* Centre—*after two or three days' wear (tab-points just beginning to lift).* Below—*well-worn shoes (breakdown at tab-points, but the backpart seams still sound).*

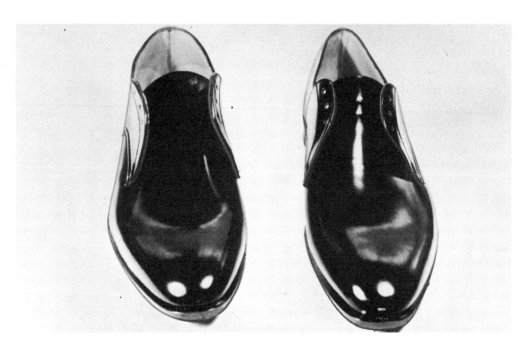

PLATE 28

Overlap Seams.

WELDED   MACHINED

Corfam

Hi-Telac

Clarino

Ortix

P.P.P.

Fig. 10.6. Types of failure given by overlap seams on various poromerics.

Fig. 10.8. Effect of heat setting on shoe shape. Both shoes on the last for 24 hours. Shoe on right was heat set.

PLATE 29

Fig. 10.14. Preformed vamps in leather (left) *and Corfam* (right).

Fig. 10.16. The Precise Edge Preforming machine.

PLATE 30

Fig. 12.1. Dressed shoe compared with undressed shoe.

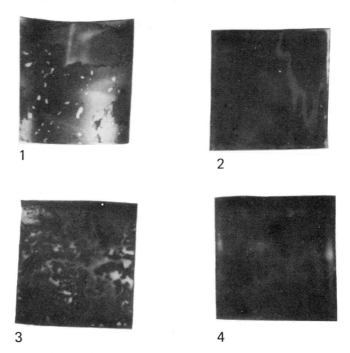

Fig. 12.6. Wetting of fillers on to cleaned and uncleaned poromerics.
1 *Uncleaned–sponge-applied filler*
2 *Cleaned–sponge-applied filler*
3 *Uncleaned–spray-applied filler*
4 *Cleaned–spray-applied filler*

PLATE 31

Fig. 13.1. Cloth-holding device in use.

Fig. 13.2. Clicking press with cloth-holding device.

PLATE 32

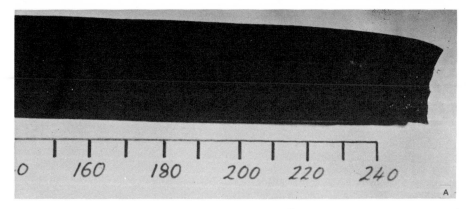

Fig. 13.4a. Effect of graded heat (140–240°C) on a poromeric.

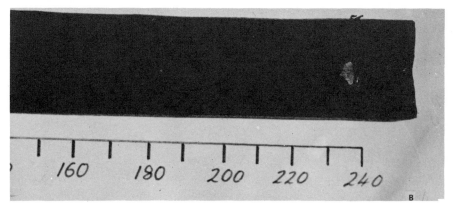

Fig. 13.4b. Effect of graded heat (140–240°C) on a poromeric.

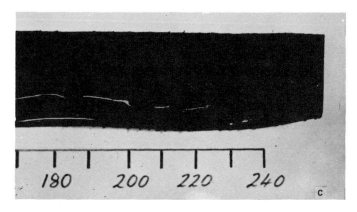

Fig. 13.4c. Effect of graded heat on a pvc.

PLATE 33

Fig. 13.5. Markings from foreign bodies during ironing-on.

Fig. 13.8. Wiper plate damage.

PLATE 34

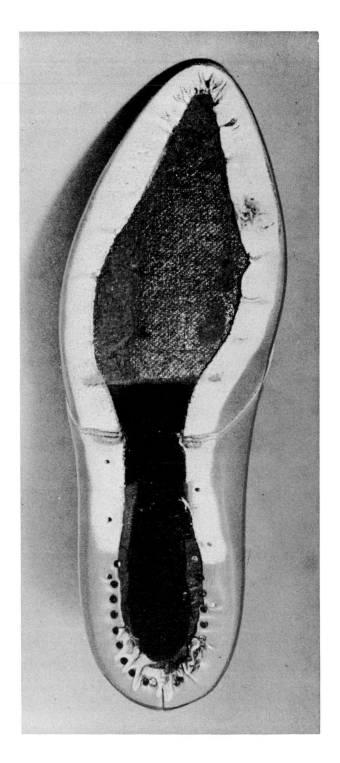

Fig. 13.9. Shoe roughed on a B.U. Automatic Upper Roughing Machine.

WEAR TRIAL SHOES

All-welded men's Gibson shoes have been worn for several weeks resulting in some weld failure at the tab-points; so far the results are too variable to inspire confidence. It is, however, fairly clear that welded overlap seams in areas not subjected to flexing would be satisfactory in wear (Fig. 10.7). One of the problems associated with welded overlap seams is surface marking and 'print through' of the underlay—this has not yet been completely overcome.

Note: In general welding results and photographs can be taken as valid only for the particular batches of materials used.

HEAT SETTING

Most of our preliminary work on the heat setting of poromerics was reported at the BBSI Conference at Harrogate in 1967. The main conclusions from this work were:

1 The shape retention of all poromerics is very poor unless an efficient heat-setting process is used
2 There are considerable variations in the setting properties of different poromerics.

To illustrate these points Table 10.2 gives the results of cold-strain setting and normal moist-heat setting on a range of poromerics.

Table 10.2. Cold-strain and moist-heat setting

Material	% set after 1 week's recovery	
	Cold-strain set [1]	Moist-heat set [2]
Corfam	21·2	62·8
Clarino	13·6	49·1
Ortix	18·0	37·2
PPP	30·4	39·2

[1] Under strain for 24 hours.
[2] 1½ min. 65°C steam, 3½ min. 110°C dry air.

A disturbing feature of this aspect of poromerics is the very poor control exercised in some factories on the heat-setting process. Check tests in a number of factories have shown some heat setters operating as much as 30% below the recommended temperature. It cannot be over emphasized that poromerics MUST have the correct setting conditions—otherwise results such as those shown in Fig. 10.8 are likely.

MOIST-HEAT SETTING

A surprising result from the heat setting work is the benefit to most poromerics of using steam as well as dry-heat treatments, i.e. moist-heat setting. Table 10.3 shows the effect of the steaming section of the moist-heat setter and also the additional benefits that can be obtained if an extra pre-steaming treatment is carried out at 85–100°C for 3 minutes.

Table 10.3. Moist-heat setting of poromerics

| Material | % set after 1 week's recovery | | |
	Dry-heat set [1]	Moist-heat set [2]	Presteamed + moist-heat set [3]
Corfam	61·6	62·8	–
PPP	47·3*	39·2*	62·6
Clarino	38·3	49·1	58·0
Ortix	28·0	37·2	56·2
Hi-Telac	–	73·2	–
Patora	42·3	51·0	64·5

* Different batches—results not strictly comparable.
[1] 5 min. hot air at 120°C.
[2] 65°C moist section, 110°C dry section.
[3] 3 min. 85°C moisture + moist-heat setting.

VARIABILITY OF SETTING BEHAVIOUR

Although in the above tables the general name of each manufacturer's poromeric has been used, there are, of course, an ever-growing number of types being developed in each case. This can lead to difficulties in commenting on the setting properties of, for example, Corfam. Table 10.4 shows the problem.

Table. 10.4. Setting behaviour of different types of Corfam

Material	% set after 1 week's recovery
Optic	59·8
Cosmos	63·6
Squaresville	61·6
Lodestar (Ladies' weight)	66·9
Lodestar (Men's weight) [1]	70·0
Lodestar (Men's weight) [2]	62·8

Moist-heat setting conditions: 1½ min. 65°C, 3½ min. 110°C.
[1], [2] Different batches.
(Cosmos and Squaresville are not at present available in the UK.)

A further complication that applies to most of the poromerics on which we have sufficient data is an unexpectedly large variation in the set figures obtained over a period of time from different batches of supposedly the same material. It is hoped that once the manufacturing processes have stabilized, these variations will reduce considerably.

DOUBLE TREATMENTS

A well-used technique when sample shoes have been made in factories is to 'ensure' good setting by repeating the heat-setting treatment at least once. Table 10.5 indicates that some improvement is given, but it is more efficient to increase the setting temperature (at least in the temperature range normally used in factories).

Table 10.5. Effect of double setting treatment

Material	% set after 1 week's recovery		
	Moist-heat setting 65°C/110°C	2 cycles 65°C/110°C	Moist-heat setting 65°C/120°C
PPP	36·4	44·3	43·7
Corfam	63·6	74·8	74·0
Ortix	42·0	46·4	49·5
Hi-Telac	73·8	81·0	74·2
Clarino	50·5	56·5	55·6

EFFECT OF SETTING TEMPERATURE

Is it practicable to improve the set of poromerics by raising the dry air temperature in the heat setter? Figs 10.9-10.13 show typical set-temperature curves for five poromerics and include the effect of a pre-steaming treatment.

It is clear from these that increasing the temperature can give improved set up to 140°C—above this temperature set can fall with some poromerics. There is, of course, a limiting factor on the temperatures that can be used, namely damage to other shoe components.

Our recommendation for an acceptable shape retention is a set of at least 60% after one week's recovery. This gives a shape roughly equivalent to that of a leather shoe which has been on the last for 3-4 days. It is not possible to achieve this set with normal dry heat setting on unlined PPP, Ortix, Clarino or Patora. Figs 10.9-10.13 show, however, that a pre-steaming treatment can lead to acceptable shape retention.

EFFECT OF LININGS

Another way of improving set is to line the upper, although here again the solution is not straightforward. The type of lining must be carefully chosen. Not surprisingly, the best lining material to give good shape

137

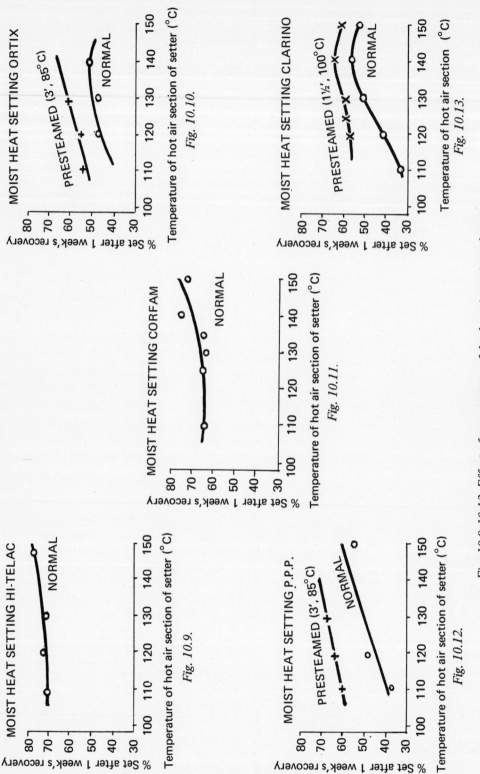

Figs 10.9–10.13. Effect of temperature of dry hot-air section of setter on set of different poromerics

retention is leather. Table 10.6 shows the effect of loose and bonded leather and fabric linings.

*Table 10.6. Effect of linings on the set of poromerics after moist-heat setting**

Material	% set after 1 week's recovery with:					
	No lining	Bonded leather lining	Loose leather lining	Loose fabric lining	Bonded fabric lining A	Bonded fabric lining B
Corfam	68·3	82·4	83·3	76·3	82·5	74·8
Clarino	49·6	66·0	70·9	48·6	60·8	47·2
Hi-Telac	78·2	83·1	82·7	75·5	74·6	74·8
Ortix	43·0	–	–	45·6	62·0	51·0
PPP	46·3	–	–	44·2	59·3	48·7

* Normal leather conditions—1½ min. at 65°C, moist; 3½ min. at 120°C, dry.

The study of the effect of linings on shape retention is obviously an important one—other aspects such as the effect of linings on fold sharpness and flexing endurance could be equally important.

EFFECT OF HEAT SETTING ON PROPERTIES

Before moist-heat setting became commercially available a considerable amount of work was carried out to ensure that the properties of leather were not harmfully affected by the process. The results of our initial experiments on poromerics are shown in Table 10.7.

The mean tear strength is not significantly affected by heat setting but the load required to start a tear may be slightly lowered.

The modulus of some materials is slightly increased (particularly Corfam) but this increase is less than that found with many leathers.

Permeability changes are generally not significant although Clarino has shown an increase and PPP a decrease in permeability after heat setting. Permeability changes are affected by the type of finish and it would be wise to check the actual material to be used.

The laminar peeling strength of Corfam is appreciably increased.

PREFORMING

Preforming—as the name implies—is the shaping of all or part of the upper before the normal lasting operation. In the work reported here the Precise Edge Preforming (PEP) machine has been used. This is designed to form the whole vamp of the upper, including the toe, before the vamp is attached to the quarters. Fig. 10.14 shows a preformed vamp in Corfam, compared with a leather vamp.

It has not been found possible to form poromerics using the normal

Table 10.7. Effect of heat setting on the properties of poromerics

The results quoted are for the ratio $\dfrac{\text{Value after heat setting}}{\text{Value on control material}}$

Material	Tear Test		Young's modulus	WVP	Laminar peeling load (mean load)
	Mean tear	Initial tear			
Corfam	0·9	0·7	1·7	0·8	1·4
	1·3	1·8	1·3		2·1
Hi-Telac	0·9	0·9	1·3	0·8	1·2
	1·0	0·7	1·1		0·9
Clarino	—	0·7	1·2	1·3	0·8
	0·9	1·0	1·3		0·9
Ortix	1·3	1·8	0·9	1·0	0·8
	0·8	0·7	0·9		0·8
PPP	0·9	1·0	1·3	0·7	—
	—	1·1	1·3		

Note: There are significant batch-to-batch variations in reaction to heat setting and until more detailed work is vompleted values lying in the range 0·8–1·2 cannot be considered to show a significant change in properties. The two results quoted for each material are from tests carried out along and across the roll.

'leather' preforming conditions, i.e. a hot metal mould with water sprayed on the flesh side of the leather.

The material would be very hot, and consequently plastic, at the end of the moulding sequence; hence the fall-in would be excessive. Work involving the pre-heating of the material followed by forming on a cold mould has been much more promising.

After examining the use of radiant, high-frequency and hot-air pre-heating prior to cold-mould forming, it was found that a simple hot-air oven gave adequate results when combined with a heated loading plate on the PEP machine. Fig. 10.15 shows the arrangement in diagrammatic form and Fig. 10.16 shows a photograph of the machine in use.

The sequence of operation is:
1 Pre-heat the vamp for 40-80 secs in air at 130°C (air speed 10 ft/sec)
2 Remove and place on loading plate (heated to 130°C)
3 The vamp is automatically loaded into the edge-clamping plates
4 When the vamp is fully shaped cold air is blown on to the grain surface.

The dwell time on the mould is 10 seconds.

The vamp temperature changes during this sequence are shown in Fig. 10.17.

The shape retention given by various poromerics with this treatment is shown in Table 10.8; the normal range of sets for preformed leather is

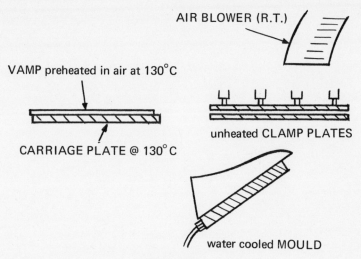

AIR BLOWER (R.T.)

VAMP preheated in air at 130°C

CARRIAGE PLATE @ 130°C

unheated CLAMP PLATES

water cooled MOULD

Fig. 10.15.

Fig. 10.15. Diagram of PEP machine as set up for preforming poromerics. (Readers are reminded that in the PEP machine the carriage plate moves to the right to load the vamp so that it is gripped by horseshoe-shaped clamping plates and that the mould then moves upwards to project through the horseshoe and thus preform the vamp. For preforming leather, the carriage plate would be cold and the mould hot and there would be no cooling-air blower.)

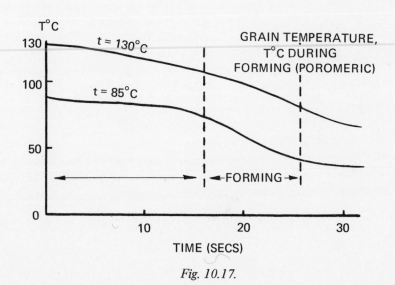

Fig. 10.17.

Fig. 10.17. Temperature of 'grain' of poromeric at different stages of preforming operation for two different temperatures (t) of the pre-heating and loading carriage

141

given for comparison, although the methods of measurement are not strictly comparable.

Table 10.8. Set obtainable by modified PEP preforming

Material	Pre-heating times (sec)	% set after 1 week's recovery
Hi-Telac	48	53·9
	72	62·8
Corfam	60	51·8
	75	49·3
Skailen	45	5·7
Belesa	60	52·8
	75	56·7
Side leather	Heated mould	77·6

It is clear that these particular poromerics do not preform as well as leather. For forepart forming (or blocking) a shape retention of 50% or over would give a useful degree of pre-shaping. Work is continuing on the precise edge preforming of these materials.

CONCLUSION

In the areas of welding and embossing it is impossible to generalize about poromerics as a class of material. The processes cannot be used on some poromerics while others respond well. There are indications that the 'perfectly weldable' poromeric is a practical proposition.

All poromerics must be heat set and many require more severe treatments than those used for leather. Improved shape can be achieved by the correct choice of linings.

Preforming using a pre-heating and cold-die technique can impart a useful degree of shape into most poromerics, but none preform as well as leather under the conditions used so far.

ACKNOWLEDGEMENTS

The work of emboss cutting and welding has been carried out by the team led by Mr R. W. T. Skelham and that on heat setting and preforming by those led by Mr L. W. Birch and Mr C. A. Lockwood. The author wishes to thank them all for the extensive help they gave in the preparation of this paper.

CHAPTER 11

Sole bonding to poromerics

D. PETTIT

INTRODUCTION

THERE is no need to stress the importance of sole bonding in view of
the wide usage of the stuck-on and injected-on systems of sole
attachment in the industry today. This paper will mainly cover those
aspects of the subject which can be safely based on laboratory tests,
and is particularly concerned with a comparison of roughing methods.

FACTORS AFFECTING PERFORMANCE

Table 11.1. Factors affecting sole bonds in production, wear and testing

Poromeric physical properties
Type of shoe construction
Sole weight and flexibility
Adhesive
Operative skill
Lasted margin flatness
Wear conditions
Type of test
Test rate
Test joint preparation

The first part of the table lists factors which are involved in the process
of sole bonding and subsequent performance. Most of these will be only
briefly discussed. The physical properties of poromerics have been
dealt with in detail in other papers, but they are obviously important
in the strength of poromeric/sole joints, because in the peel test it is
usually the poromeric structure which fails and not the adhesive.

The type of shoe construction will affect the weight and flexibility of
the sole, the stresses incorporated in the joint during bonding and the
stresses to which the bond is subjected in wear.

Although the adhesive must be taken into account in consideration of
bond performance in testing, adhesive or adhesion failure is rare. It,
therefore, appears that there is little general difficulty in choice
of adhesive, provided the appropriate type, e.g. polyurethane for
sticking to pvc, is chosen. The effect of production requirements on
choice of adhesive will not be dealt with.

Operative skill, particularly in preparation (roughing) of the lasted margin will have a profound effect on bond performance. There may also be a wide difference between factory and laboratory produced bonds, because of the possible presence of pleats in the lasted margin, the probable greater skill and experience of the factory operative, and the greater care which may be taken in the laboratory where high productivity is not necessary.

The flatness of the lasted margin has been referred to in other papers and is important in two respects: it will aid uniform preparation and reduce the stresses present in the stuck-on bond.

The effect of wear conditions has been covered adequately by Mr Bisson in Chapter 7, but it is clear that even if wearers did not differ markedly in their gait, the variety of stresses and strains met by the sole joint during normal wear by one typical wearer would defy reproduction in one laboratory test.

The type of test, e.g. lap shear or peel, repeated stress or static load, will govern laboratory results and probably the ranking in which a series of joints are placed. Allied to the type of test is the rate at which loads are applied, for instance, at high rates to represent impact or at low rates to allow creep of joints. It is likely that every one of these variations of test procedure will have a bearing on joint performance in wear.

TEST METHODS

WEAR EXPERIENCE

Experience of poromeric joint behaviour in wear is essential to back up our considerable experience of laboratory testing, and wear trials are now being run to improve our knowledge in this area. One large current trial is testing stuck-on and injected-on constructions for four poromerics and one leather at two levels of lasted margin preparation. The margin preparations were chosen (a) for optimum strength and (b) for somewhat less than optimum in the expectation of providing a significant failure rate. It is hoped that this trial will provide evidence of correlation between wear failures and laboratory tests on joints prepared in similar ways on the same materials.

In addition, we have substantial experience, gleaned from our own and our members' efforts, in the production of poromeric shoes with bonded soles. This means that we are fairly well grounded in the problems associated with these types of constructions and what processes or steps to better bonding are practicable.

STANDARD PEEL TEST

The laboratory test which will be most widely referred to in this report is our standard peel test. In this a joint, one inch in width, prepared from the adhesive and upper and sole materials in question (with as close adherence to factory procedure as possible) is peeled apart at a rate of 6 in/min. (jaw separation). The specimen jaws operate in a straight line and the joint finds its own angle of repose according to the stiffness of the two materials making up the joint. This is the test used most frequently in reporting to shoe manufacturers on the effect on joint strength of changing process variables or adhesives. The test is very informative used in this way, but care must be taken in predicting joint behaviour in wear and in comparing the strengths of joints made up with different materials.

It is, therefore, stressed that although such peel test results will be used here to compare the effect of, e.g. roughing on the joint strengths of a large number of poromerics, it is dangerous to compare the strength characteristics of poromerics with these results alone. It is likely that differences in modulus of poromerics will have different effects on joint behaviour in wear compared with their effects in the standard peel test.

MANDREL TEST

One obvious way in which the shoe joints differ from the laboratory peel test joints is that the upper material is backed by a stiff insole. Therefore, loads applied to the upper material are distributed over a wider area, and separation of the upper material from the sole will require higher loads than when the backing is absent.

The SATRA 'Toe Tester' provides a suitable test, but complete shoes represent expensive test pieces if you wish to know the destructive load. We have tried a cheaper version which we call the Mandrel[1] Test. A test piece is made in the form of a one-inch wide section of a shoe on a semi-circular mandrel as in Fig. 11.1. This is then tested on the SATRA 'Toe Tester'.

Typical mandrel test results as compared with peel are given in Table 11.2.

Table 11.2. Resin rubber stuck-on joints

	Break-in loads (lb/inch width)	
	Peel test	Mandrel test
Poromeric A	20	40
Poromeric B	21	43
Poromeric C	29	48
Poromeric D	20	31

The results recorded are 'break-in loads'. A break-in load is a feature of peel testing of many poromerics. A higher load is required to break through the first layer to an interface between two layers of the poromeric; subsequent failure is then usually at a lower load along a frequently weaker interface.

This dual nature of poromeric joint behaviour makes results difficult to interpret. However, it is clear that 'break-in' occurs at substantially

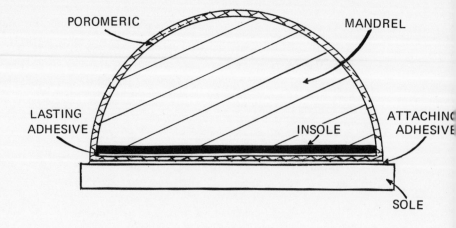

Fig. 11.1. The Mandrel Test. (To simulate the SATRA toe-test)

higher figures in the mandrel test than in the unbacked peel test. A
similar rise is also found for leather joints.

SLOW SPEED PEEL TEST

Two poromerics which have received much investigation are Corfam and
Clarino. In addition to standard peel tests of joints made with these
materials, slow speed peel tests at a rate of 1/20 in/min. have been
carried out. These did not contribute any useful information on the
behaviour of the poromerics. However, when rubber failure was induced,
this occurred at lower loads than at peel rates of 6 in/min. It does not
appear from our results to date that slow speed peel will prove useful
except that potential cohesive weakness of the adhesive is likely to be
demonstrated.

IMPACT TEST

The next test under development is an impact test to represent toe
stubbing in wear. SATRA has, in the past, used a form of pendulum
to provide high rates of load application, but at the moment we use the
simpler device of a falling weight to apply sudden loads. The destructive
work done to the sample is altered by the distance the weight falls. It appears
to be useful in demonstrating any tendencies towards non-coalescence
in adhesive joints, but we have had insufficient experience to date of its
uses in testing poromerics to form any conclusions as to its use in
predicting behaviour in wear.

146

FATIGUE TESTS

Some form of fatigue test is frequently suggested as an alternative to the peel test for predicting wear behaviour. In this a repeated loading cycle is applied to a joint with a peak load considerably less than the static failure load. We have not neglected this type of test, and are currently using a six-station tester which loads a 2 sq cm lap shear joint with 20 lb for 50% of a time cycle of 1·12 seconds. The test is being applied to joints made from poromerics concurrently being tested in a wear trial. This test, however, is particularly susceptible to alteration of the loading cycle by stretch and set of the joint materials. Ways of avoiding this alteration are being investigated.

COMPARISON OF PREPARATION METHODS

The most favoured method of roughing is to use a light gauge wire brush (39 swg). We have found advantages, in the laboratory, of using a slower speed, i.e. 1 400 rpm as against the usual speed of 3 000 rpm used on leather roughing machines.

This may be a reflection on the comparative lack of skill in the laboratory, and skilled factory operators may use the higher speed to obtain higher production rates. It has also been found advisable to blunt the brush by applying the carborundum to the brush whilst rotating in the direction of use. A few poromerics with a hard surface skin are not amenable to a blunt brush and a sharpened brush may be required to get through this skin.

This requirement of poromerics to have the surface prepared for optimum adhesion is a disappointing one. One would have thought that inherent good adhesion and surface strength could have been built into man-made materials, and would give them a very real advantage over leather. Indeed a few poromerics illustrate that this can be done.

In considering and presenting these laboratory results on a range of materials it was found that a fair spread of both failure load and type existed. This made it difficult to prepare meaningful averages and the figures shown are typical ones. The results are presented as a guide to the degree of roughing that should be aimed at, and comparison between poromerics of quoted failure loads may be misleading. The results will be dealt with in two groups, the first dealing with those poromerics having no woven interlayer and the second with those having an interlayer.

(a) POROMERICS WITH NO WOVEN INTERLAYER

CLARINO 1000

The recommended scratch rough, just into the microcellular layer, provides a high breaking-in load. The delamination strength is good,

Table 11.3. No woven interlayer—Recommended roughing: light, not beyond cellular layer.

Roughing	Joint strength (lb/inch)			
	Stuck-on		Injected-on	
Scratch	(36)*	22	(30)*	15
To non-woven base	28–36		20	

* Figures in brackets are 'break-in' loads. Other figures are steady failure loads usually resulting from some form of delamination.

but is apparently rather lower on injected than on stuck-on joints. These results imply that one would get a joint of higher eventual strength by roughing into the base layer. However, this carries a danger of roughing too deeply and weakening the base. The manufacturer's recommendation is, therefore, sound policy and provides a good bond.

HI-TELAC BD

Table 11.4. No woven interlayer—Recommended roughing: scratch

Preparation	Joint strength (lb/inch)			
	Stuck-on		Injected-on	
None	(24)	11	(11)	8
MEK wiped	(24)	12	(12)	8
Scratch roughed	(27)	12	(13)	8
Roughed to non-woven base*		30		40

* Carries danger of over-roughing.

This presents a similar picture of a high break-in load and again, although roughing to the base provides the best bond, the risk of over-roughing and weakening means that a scratch rough is the safest practical aim. This will, in fact, provide stronger keying areas because uneven lasted margins will usually mean localized deep roughing.

ORTIX (LADIES' WEIGHT)

Roughing just into the cellular layer is again advocated and the results here are representative of a large number of tests. It is interesting to note that the break-in load is apparently affected by the adhesive. The

148

reason for this is not fully understood but might be associated with the modulus, i.e. a softer adhesive leads to high break-in loads.

Table 11.5. (Ladies' weight 1·0 mm)–No woven interlayer–Recommended roughing: light.

Light rough	Strength of stuck-on joints (lb/inch)	
1-part neoprene	(20)	6
2-part neoprene	(10)	6
Premixed urethane to pvc	(23)	5

EXPERIMENTAL POROMERIC A

Table 11.6. No woven interlayer–Recommended roughing: uncertain

Preparation	Joint strength (lb/inch)			
	Stuck-on		Injected-on	
None	(30)	7		20
MEK wipe		20*	(21)	8
Scratch rough	(25)	10	(12)	8
Roughed to non-woven base		12		11

* Rubber failed.

Here again a scratch rough would be advocated to eliminate dangers associated with deep roughing. Here, as in others of the poromerics, it is tempting to advise no roughing or solvent wiping; in the absence of results from other tests or wear trials, however, this would be risky.

EXPERIMENTAL POROMERIC B

Table 11.7. No woven interlayer–Recommended roughing: not known.

Preparation	Joint strength (lb/inch)	
	Stuck-on	Injected-on
None	5	2
MEK wipe	10	9
Scratch rough	*10*	*10*
Rough to non-woven base†	20*	30

† Danger of over-roughing.   * Rubber failed.

149

This appears to call for deep roughing to give a satisfactory bond, but factory experience would be necessary to determine whether this could be done without occasional weakening of the base.

POROUS PLASTICS POROMERIC

Table 11.8. No fibrous layer—Recommended roughing: none necessary.

Preparation	Joint strength (lb/inch)	
	Stuck-on	Injected-on
None	23	18
MEK wiped	24	19
Roughed	32	21

This calls for the minimum of preparation. Solvent wiping is not practicable as it could cause unsightly swelling at the featherline. There is apparently a slight benefit in roughing, and this might well be provided sufficiently by the steps necessary to flatten the lasted margin.

(b) POROMERICS WITH WOVEN INTERLAYER

The second group of poromerics have a woven interlayer. Under strain, they frequently show a tendency to separate at the interfaces of the woven layer with the other layers. Thus one again gets a higher break-in load and a lower delamination load as failure continues along a weak interface. However, if the cellular layer is very stretchy the break-in load may be misleadingly high in that delamination will occur in the peel test at loads insufficient to break the cellular layer. In the shoe the same type of failure may well occur. It, therefore, appears common sense to eliminate the chance of this type of failure by complete removal of the cellular layer.

HI-TELAC CF

Table 11.9. Woven interlayer—Recommended roughing: progressively deeper from feather inwards, through to non-woven base.

Roughing	Joint strength (lb/inch)			
	Stuck-on		Injected-on	
Scratch	(20)	10	(18)	6
To woven layer	(20)	10	(26)	11
To non-woven base		24		23

150

The recommended rough, down to the woven layer, seems the best preparation, and provided the cellular layer is removed close to the feather no delamination failures should occur.

BELESA

Table 11.10. *Woven interlayer—Recommended roughing: not known.*

Preparation	Joint strength (lb/inch)			
	Stuck-on		Injected-on	
None	(34)	5	(17)	5
MEK wipe	(35)	6	(19)	4
Scratch rough	(31)	6	(20)	4
Rough to woven layer	(35)	11	(21)	9

This material has a good break-in load but the low delamination load would cause concern in a man's shoe, particularly in the light of leather experience. Even when the break-in load is as high as that found, the chance of roughing or impact damage, leaving one relying on the interlaminar strength, hardly seems worth taking. This material needs roughing to the woven layer.

EXPERIMENTAL POROMERIC C

Table 11.11. *Woven interlayer—Recommended roughing: not known.*

Preparation	Joint strength (lb/inch)			
	Stuck-on		Injected-on	
None	(26)	8		8
Light rough	(33)	8	(14)	7
Roughed to woven layer	(28)	18	(20)	14

The evidence of peel tests points to the need to rough to the woven layer.

CORFAM

This poromeric has been examined in greater detail than most. Scratch roughing (just into the cellular layer) appears to carry with it the risk of laminar failure at low loads.

Roughing to the woven layer is called for and is relatively easy to do in a uniform manner. However, it was clear that it was possible to damage the woven layer during the roughing operation allowing a breakthrough at variable loads into a second interface (woven/non-woven) of relatively low strength. Because of the usual configuration difference found in a woven fabric—tight warp and loose weft threads—it was considered that the direction of roughing might influence the degree of damage produced.

Table 11.12. Corfam (Lodestar)—Woven interlayer— Recommended roughing: to woven layer

Preparation		Joint strength (lb/inch) Stuck-on			
Roughing		Along roll		Across roll	
Scratch		(22)	7	(17)	5
To woven layer	Right angles to peel		25	(16-26)*	4
	Parallel to peel		20		20
To non-woven base		24		23	

* Tearing of fabric.

The results shown (Table 11.12) for joints roughed to the woven layer seem to bear this out. The failures were mainly adhesion to woven layer failure, but when the peel test was performed across the roll (parallel to weft threads) and roughing had been at right angles to the direction of tests, considerable tearing of the fabric took place (figures in brackets in

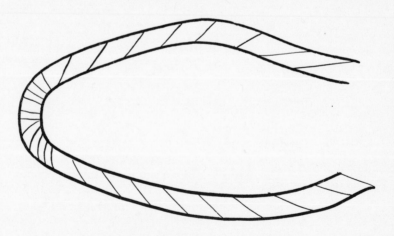

Fig. 11.2. Lasted Corfam Margin. Lines represent direction of "tight" woven layer fibres (along roll)

Table 11.12), indicating damage to the weft threads. These are, in fact, the circumstances under which it would have been predicted that damage would be likely to occur.

The next table (11.13) for injected-on pvc joints shows a similar trend and maximum bond strength (minimum of fabric tearing) occurs when roughing parallel to and peeling along the warp.

Table 11.13. Corfam (Lodestar)

Preparation		Strength of injected-on joints (lb/inch)			
Roughing		Along roll		Across roll	
Scratch			8		8
To woven layer	Right angles to peel	(14–20)*	5–20	(12)*	4
	Parallel to peel	(20–40)*	8–20	(18)*	4
To non-woven base			14		14

* Tearing of fabric.

Fig. 11.2 represents the lasted margin of a Corfam upper (cut tight toe to heel) and the lines represent the direction of tight threads (warp). Following the evidence of Tables 11.12 and 11.13 it appears there may be an overall advantage in the operative attempting (if practicable) to rough in the direction of the lines.

Having examined the problem of roughing down to the woven layer with the minimum of damage it is evident that adhesive performance may not be all one would wish, judging by the amount of adhesion to woven layer failure found in the joints tested.

Table 11.14. Corfam (Lodestar)–Effect of adhesive on strength of injected-on joints. Preparation–hand peeled to woven layer. Tested across roll

Adhesive system		lb/inch
Premixed urethane	1 coat	23
Premixed urethane	2 coats	32
Premixed urethane, 1 coat after THF wipe		27+
2-component urethane	1 coat	17
2-component urethane, heat reactivated		30–40
2-component urethane, after DR wipe		34
2-component urethane, after SDP.102 wipe		24
2-component urethane	2 coats	23

THF–tetrahydrofuran; DR–Desmodur R; SDP.102; a Satra product.

Table 11.14 indicates the effect of different adhesives and priming treatments on injected-on joints prepared to the woven layer of Corfam. The Corfam for these joints was prepared by peeling the microcellular layer away to leave the woven layer undamaged. This was done so that weakness in the woven layer should not interfere with the testing of the adhesive systems.

These results show clearly ways of improving the bond of injected-on soles. The beneficial effect of heat reactivating the adhesive-coated upper, suggested by one of Du Pont's technical staff, was surprisingly effective. However, heat reactivation may not fit in with all production lines and here a wipe with a 10% solution of isocyanate (Desmodur R) proved effective in raising the bond strength. This particular treatment has not yet been investigated fully enough to give the optimum conditions but is clearly worth further study.

COMPARISON WITH LEATHER

Some typical failure loads are given for leather joints in Table 11.15.

Table 11.15. Leather joints (lb/inch) Full chrome cow

	Full grain	Corrected grain
RR–Neoprene	12–20	20–30
PVC–PU	15–20	20–30
Injected pvc–PU	12–35	15–50
Ladies' 4 PU adhesives	12–20	–

The first figure represents light roughing and the second figure a normal rough to the corium layer. It seems that well-roughed leather will give bond strengths higher than most poromerics, but this is not always the case. The last figures in the table represent the average for four polyurethane adhesives on a typical leather used in ladies' stuck-on work. These materials were chosen after a survey of 12 factories producing ladies' stuck-on shoes. Judging by the standard of preparation observed, typical production sole bonds would lie in the 12–20 lb/inch range.

At the moment it is difficult to suggest values for sole bonds for satisfactory sole attachment to poromerics in wear. In fact, although SATRA has suggested guide figures for leather stuck-on work, these have not been well established. Taking into account the variability of leather bonds it is likely that such figures as we do have in mind for leather need to be revised downwards for poromerics. In any case it would not be wise to compare poromerics and leather solely on the basis of the standard rate peel test.

STUDIES OF STRAIN DISTRIBUTION IN TEST JOINTS

In addition to the empirical approach to the meaning of laboratory tests mentioned above, we are engaged in a more fundamental examination of their significance. This has been begun by photographic studies of the failure of poromeric joints in the peel test. Simple photography has done little more than confirm by visual record the type of behaviour we suspected. However, we have been able to extend this by photoelastic studies to show the distribution of strains in a joint under stress.

For this work joints were made up of poromerics and transparent pvc soling material of roughly the same hardness as used in footwear soling. The pvc was laminated to resin rubber to give a material of the correct thickness. 2 mm sections of the joints were cut and photographed under stress by electronic flash between crossed plates of polarizing material (Polaroid). The 35 mm camera and lens system provided an image/object magnification of about 2·7

The figures represent the pattern of isochromatic and isoclinic fringes observed. Each isochromatic fringe represents a stress of 50 g/mm^2. The pvc layer showing the fringes is about 1·5 mm wide.

Fig. 11.3 represents Clarino prepared by a scratch rough and it appears that the adhesive is applying considerable stress to the sole in front of the upper/sole juncture.

Fig. 11.4 represents Corfam scratch roughed and illustrates how the pattern of stress is spread out compared with the Clarino joint.

Fig. 11.5 again shows a similar joint to that in Fig. 11.4, but in a more advanced state of failure. Here the delamination of the microcellular and woven layers has caused a division of the stress in the sole into two distinct areas. The concentration of fringes indicates that the stretched microcellular layer is bearing the major part of the load.

These investigations are in an early stage and require further work to demonstrate the relationship of the stresses in these 2 mm wide joints to those in the more familiar 2·5 cm joints. At the moment it certainly appears the most likely way of relating poromeric modulus, and perhaps adhesive modulus to the stress distribution in joints.

In conclusion, I would like to acknowledge the contributions of my colleagues to this paper, in particular those of Mr F. B. Blackwell and his assistants who have produced most of the experimental data used.

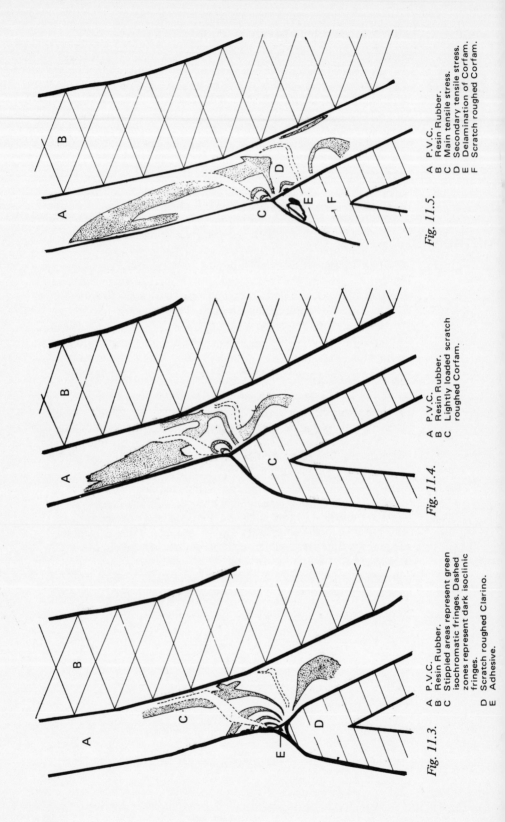

Fig. 11.3.

A   P.V.C.
B   Resin Rubber.
C   Stippled areas represent green isochromatic fringes. Dashed zones represent dark isoclinic fringes.
D   Scratch roughed Clarino.
E   Adhesive.

Fig. 11.4.

A   P.V.C.
B   Resin Rubber.
C   Lightly loaded scratch roughed Corfam.

Fig. 11.5.

A   P.V.C.
B   Resin Rubber.
C   Main tensile stress.
D   Secondary tensile stress.
E   Delamination of Corfam.
F   Scratch roughed Corfam.

156

CHAPTER 12

Shoe finishes for poromerics

B. D. ROE

INTRODUCTION

LEATHER shoes are dressed essentially to give them a kind handle and a pleasant appearance to ensure customer appeal. The upper leather used, as received from the tannery, may well fulfil these requirements. But by the time the leather has passed through the making stages of shoe production, it will have an accumulation of factory dirt and damages, resulting in a comparatively battered appearance.

So the shoe room has to restore the shoes to a saleable state, and this includes dressing them to achieve this. Fig. 12.1 compares a dressed with an undressed shoe.

The dressing operations normally involve three stages.

Firstly, the shoes are cleaned to remove factory dirt and grease, and to prepare or condition the surface ready for the next coat. This second step is the filler coat which gives fill, enhances the colour and provides a surface for the easy acceptance of the top dressing. The top dressing, usually spray applied, gives the desired handle and lustre, and bears the brunt of resistance in wear.

Variations in this three-stage process are common, involving the elimination of one or more stages.

Dressing also includes ancillary operations such as repairing or antiquing.

The shoe manufacturer requires that these dressing operations should be easy to carry out, with simple and reproducible control of performance. Fig. 12.2 depicts the dressing operations, cleaner, filler, top dressing, etc.

Typical Dressing Procedure

Cleaner–To remove dirt, grease, cement. Condition surface for filler application.

Filler–Improves fill. Enhances depth of colour.

Top dressing–Gives kind handle and pleasant appearance of the required lustre.

Ancillary operations–Repairing, antiquing, pearlizing, upper decoration.

Fig. 12.2.

The customer wants his or her shoes to look nice, both when bought and during wear. Traditional dressings only contribute to the appearance before wear; during the first few days' wear the dressing will gradually be removed, and brush and polish will be necessary to maintain a reasonable appearance. (In fact it has been claimed that a good leather shoe cannot be properly polished up until the dressing has been removed.) Up till now these dressings have been perfectly adequate, but the advent of poromerics may change the situation, as discussed later.

Poromeric shoes are dressed for exactly the same reasons, that is, to upgrade the appearance. It was initially thought that poromerics would not require dressing as such, only cleaning. But dressing the shoe enables a range of lustres to be obtained and considerably enhances the depth of colour. Consequently poromerics are frequently dressed, although it is quite usual simply to clean and polish up in one operation, otherwise leaving them in the natural state.

Basically the same operations of cleaning, fillering, and spraying, etc, are used as for leather but some modifications in technique and materials used are necessary. This is partly because of differences in structure between poromerics and leather, and partly because improved performance is demanded by the poromeric manufacturers from the dressings used with their products.

PERFORMANCE OF DRESSINGS ON POROMERICS

Poromerics are generally more resistant to scuffing and wet rubbing than most leathers. In wear, therefore, a poromeric surface will not deteriorate so much, enabling simple cleaning by means of a damp cloth—that is, the appearance is easily maintained and the shoes are said to have 'easy care' properties. This is what is claimed and there seems to be no reason to disagree with this.

Since easy care is possible with the straight poromeric, and because poromeric manufacturers want to retain these properties, dressings used on their materials should also confer the benefits of easy care.

A typical specification for a dressed poromeric is:

Vamp flexing:	No whitening or flaking afte 100 000 SATRA vamp flexes.
Water spotting:	No marking after a drop of water has been on the surface for 15 minutes.
Wet rub:	No marking after at least 512 SATRA wet rubs.

Tests are normally carried out 4–7 days after dressing.

A dressed poromeric meeting this specification will confer the same properties of easy care as the untreated material.

SURFACE STRUCTURE OF POROMERICS

Before considering the dressings used to achieve this performance it is worth discussing the surface structure of poromerics, since this is partly responsible for the need for modified dressings.

The surface layer of poromerics is the only part that affects or is affected by dressings. This layer may be acrylic, nitrocellulose or

158

NITROCELLULOSE (FOR LEATHER)

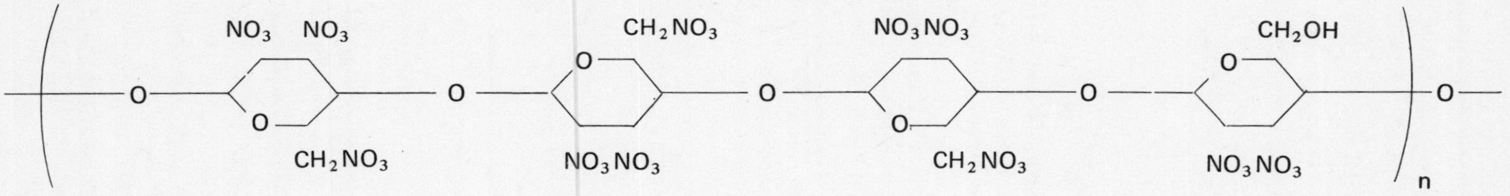

POLYURETHANE (FOR POROMERICS)

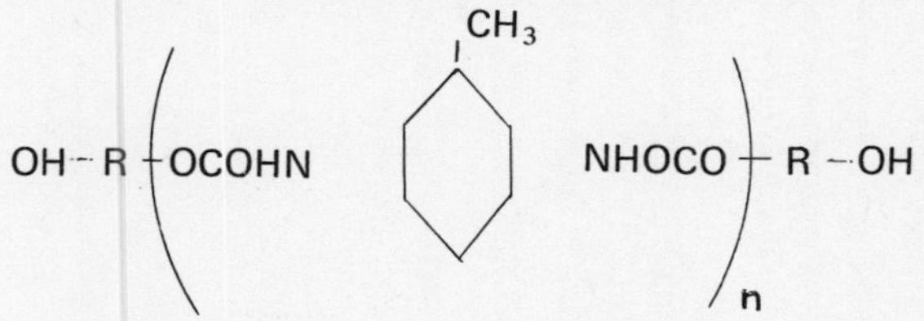

Fig. 12.3. Chemical formulae of polymers used in finishes.

159

polyurethane, most likely the latter, and although it is only about 0·005 mm to 0·025 mm thick it has a great effect on the behaviour of materials applied to it.

This is particularly true for wetting out of coatings, whether they be dressings or other finishes, or adhesives. Good wetting is necessary to achieve levelness of the coating and good adhesion, although for the latter good wetting is not the only criterion. There should also be some similarity in chemical type. It is the chemical type of the surface which determines how easily it will be wetted by a coating.

Leather is typically finished with a nitrocellulose film, or less frequently with a fixed protein. The chemical structure of a polyurethane and nitrocellulose is given in Fig. 12.3.

WETTING ON TO A POROMERIC SURFACE

These different types of surface have different surface energies, or surface tensions, and react differently to wetting out of coatings. A coating on a surface produces three interfaces—the liquid coating in contact with the surface, the liquid coating in contact with the atmosphere, and the surface in contact with the atmosphere (as shown in Fig. 12.4). The surface energies at these interfaces balance out, resulting in the equation $\gamma_{AS} = \gamma_{CS} + \gamma_{CA} \cos \theta$ where γ = surface energy and θ is the angle of contact. The contact angle thus depends on the surface energy of the three interfaces. It can be shown from this equation that wetting occurs when the energy of the coating/surface interface is less than the energy of the

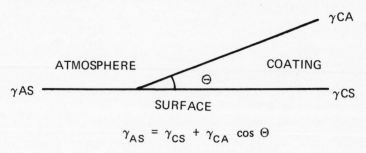

$$\gamma_{AS} = \gamma_{CS} + \gamma_{CA} \cos \Theta$$

Fig. 12.4. Interfacial tensions.

surface/atmosphere interface; that is, when the new surface has a lower resultant energy. This condition applies when the contact angle θ is less than 90°. When the reverse applies, i.e. contact angle $> 90°$, then poor wetting will occur. Strictly speaking perfect wetting only occurs with a contact angle of zero, and complete non-wetting only when the contact angle is 180°. 90° is taken by convention to be the dividing line, between good wetting and poor wetting. (Fig. 12.5 shows the shapes of a droplet on a surface illustrating good wetting and poor wetting, e.g. water on glass wets, water on paraffin wax does not wet well.)

Applied to the surfaces which are under consideration, that is, polyurethane for poromerics and nitrocellulose for leather, the surface energies and contact angles of a water-based coating on these surfaces are such that wetting is poor on polyurethanes and better, though not perfect, on nitrocellulose.

This means that polyurethanes are more resistant to a good level application of a water-based dressing. In fact, solvent-based coatings have a lower energy and a reduced contact angle on a polyurethane surface compared to aqueous dressings, and wet out much better. Some poromeric manufacturers do in fact recommend that solvent-based dressings in the form of solution or lacquer emulsion are used, rather than water-based dressings, and on the Continent and elsewhere this is quite typical practice. Water-based dressings are not advised because of difficulty in wetting and ensuring good adhesion.

But in this country, solvent-based dressings are not liked, quite

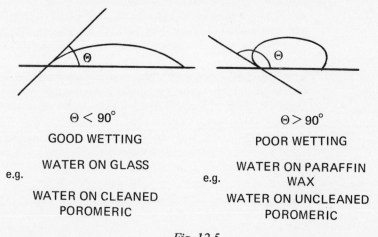

| $\Theta < 90°$ | $\Theta > 90°$ |
| GOOD WETTING | POOR WETTING |

e.g. WATER ON GLASS   e.g. WATER ON PARAFFIN WAX

WATER ON CLEANED POROMERIC   WATER ON UNCLEANED POROMERIC

Fig. 12.5.

justifiably because they are inflammable and have a consequent fire risk. High flash products or lacquer emulsions, which have less fire risk, usually have the disadvantage of a penetrating odour, which can permeate the factory and persist into the box. Solvent-based materials also have the additional drawback of higher cost.

So the problem is to produce water-based dressings which will wet easily on to polyurethane, and can be used in a similar manner to conventional leather dressings. In practice a compromise is necessary.

CLEANER

The compromise involves using a dressing system in which the first stage, that is cleaning, uses a solvent cleaner instead of the more conventional water-based cleaners for leather (although greasy resistant leathers often require a spirit cleaner).

The solvent cleaner, as well as removing dirt and grease, will modify the surface energies and condition the surface so that in the next stage, an aqueous filler will wet out easily.

But it is not quite as simple as that. Just as variations in leather necessitate a range of cleaners, so do the differences in poromerics. One solvent cleaner on poromeric A, for instance, would be quite satisfactory and enable easy wetting of the filler. The same cleaner on poromeric B would have no effect on the ability of the filler to wet out. It is even more critical than this; differences between different colours or different batches of poromerics, probably due to change in formulation of the polyurethane surface layer, have resulted in differences in wetting of a filler after cleaning. This is admittedly rather a rare occurrence, but it does indicate that the situation is likely to be a changing one.

A relatively mild solvent cleaner of the petrol type is adequate for the less resistant poromerics. For the more resistant poromeric surfaces a stronger cleaner is needed.

It is quite easy to formulate a cleaner which will enable the filler to wet out but a delicate balance is necessary to ensure that it is not too strong. That is, as well as promoting good wetting, there must be no attack of the poromerics surface, which could result in stripping or distortion of the poromeric surface. For example, a stronger cleaner would be necessary on poromeric B, but would be far too vicious on poromeric A.

For this reason, the lowest strength cleaner that is consistent with good wetting of the filler should be used. It appears that two cleaners will cover the range of poromerics now available, but stronger ones are in reserve should they ever be needed.

It is essential that this cleaning operation with poromerics is thoroughly carried out. Any areas that are missed or skimped will show up during the later operations. Careful hand cleaning or automatic machine cleaning is the basis for successful dressing of poromerics.

The foregoing deals mainly with conditioning of the surfaces by the cleaner, ready for the filler. This process will also clean off factory dirt and grease. There are no particular problems here, although poromeric surfaces seem rather more susceptible to silicone contamination than does leather. This will show up as spotting when the shoes are finally dressed. This is another reason to ensure thorough cleaning, and to avoid recontamination it is advisable to dress fairly quickly after cleaning.

Some cement marks will be cleaned off easily, but polyurethane cements, if allowed to dry, may need to be rubbed with a piece of crepe, or a different cleaner to remove them completely. Care should be taken to ensure that the poromeric surface is not damaged. The best way is to wipe off cement marks while still wet.

FILLER

Most poromerics do not need any improvement in fill—but fillers will considerably improve the depth of colour. This is especially true for black shoes. Light fillers only are required to achieve this—heavier fillers may tend to give more of a solid plastic appearance, and may not have adequate adhesion.

Once the surface has been prepared by the cleaner for good wetting out of the filler, there are no particular problems of application.

Typical leather fillers will wet out easily on to cleaned poromerics, but are not up to the standard of adhesion required to give easy care properties. Modification to the basic polymers used in the fillers are necessary to produce an affinity for the surface. Such modified fillers are readily available and these adhere so well that they virtually become an integral part of the poromeric.

These modified fillers are used in the same way as conventional fillers, that is they will normally be sponge applied, or less frequently, spray applied. Spray application will give a more even streak-free result, but unless linings are dark coloured or great care is taken, can be used only for non-black work. It should be noted that these types of filler are based on more resistant polymers and if allowed to dry out will be difficult to remove. It is advisable to clean sponges or spraying equipment straight after use. Sponges will benefit from soaking in diluted ammonia to keep them clean and soft. Figure 12.6 shows the wetting of fillers on to cleaned and uncleaned poromerics.

TOP DRESSING

The final stage is the top dressing, usually spray applied. This too must stand up to the specification which means that good wet rub resistance and good adhesion (to the filler) is required. Conventional wax-type dressings do not have sufficient wet rub resistance—they are normally removed after 1-8 SATRA wet rubs. This has no adverse effects during wear of leather shoes because brush and polish will adequately maintain the appearance and wear properties.

But when 'easy care' is claimed, that is not good enough. Resin-based dressings must be used, but not just any resin. Not all resins, including some types used in present-day top dressings, will improve wet rub resistance. Resins which will give more durable dressings, such as have become available over the last few years, are necessary.

More durable top dressings were introduced some years ago for leather, with the specific purpose of giving a degree of easy care to leather shoes. They have not yet become widely used in the Trade mainly because conventional dressings do a reasonable job anyway, and there is just no demand for an improved performance. However, now that poromerics are being more widely used and advertised, it is expected that leather shoes will eventually have to offer the same easy care properties.

To illustrate this point, several years ago a wear trial comparing these durable dressings and the older dressings on leather was set up. A number of unsolicited comments were received during the trial, reporting favourably on the way shoes were retaining their appearance. On checking, it was found that all shoes commented on were dressed with the more durable version. The final analysis of replies to questions about wear and appearance after six months confirmed that the durable dressings gave improved results. A separate part of the trial concerned with cleaning methods proved that easy care maintenance with a damp cloth was all that was necessary to retain a smart appearance.

Trials on poromerics, using these durable top dressings as part of the system, showed that they gave results meeting the specification, when

163

used with the cleaners and fillers detailed earlier, and these are now being used.

If for any reason these dressings have to be cleaned off, this should be done as soon as possible. Once they have dried out, very strong solvents or heavy rubbing are needed and this could adversely affect the poromeric surface.

SIMPLIFIED DRESSING SYSTEMS

With leather shoes, simplified dressing systems are possible, and are fairly widely used. Although the final results with such simple systems are not up to the full 3-process dressing operation, they can give a quite reasonable appearance. These simpler systems usually involve missing out the cleaning or filling processes, or both.

With poromerics, there is less scope for these more economic processes. Cleaning is essential, and the only possibility is to omit the filler, with some consequent loss in appearance. If this is done, it is the top dressing which has to wet out and adhere to the cleaned poromeric surface. Wetting out is no problem, whether by sponge or spray application, but adhesion may be reduced on some poromerics. It is always wise to check that such simplified systems meet acceptable standards.

SOLVENT-BASED DRESSINGS

Solvent-based dressings, as mentioned earlier, have a number of disadvantages. Nevertheless they are available in solution form or as lacquer emulsions. They have the advantage that they wet out more easily on to polyurethanes and cleaning is not so critical, and they also have good adhesion and wet rub properties. They are, however, very rarely used, and for all-round convenience, ease of use and performance the aqueous dressings are superior.

ANCILLARY OPERATIONS

REPAIRING

Ancillary operations such as repairing or antiquing form part of the dressing operations in the shoe room.

With regard to repairing, the best answer is still to try to avoid it. Conventional leather repairers have poor adhesion and flexibility when applied to poromerics, and can flake off, particularly on large areas. In practice it seems that a reasonable amount of care will virtually eliminate the need for repairing.

If, however, small marks or grazes occur they can be adequately repaired with a hard crayon, or with a mist spray of solvent repairer, provided that adhesion and flexibility are checked.

DECORATIVE EFFECTS

ANTIQUING AND SHADOW SPRAYING

Shadow sprays, as used for leather can be used with no trouble, using conventional techniques. Spirit dye solutions or nitrocellulose solutions can be used to give special effects, such as producing a two-colour effect, on poromerics. Similar materials can be used as an all-over variant; for example, to change a reddish brown to a darker brown.

All these types of products are solvent-based, and no particular application problems are encountered.

PEARLIZING

This is a simple operation which can considerably upgrade the appearance. All that is necessary is to use a mild petrol cleaner, followed by application of the pearlized dressing. Strong cleaners are not necessary even on the most resistant poromerics, since the pearlized dressing is solvent-based and wets out well. Care has to be taken to obtain consistent and reproducible colouring, since pearl dressings are rather delicate and transparent colours.

PATTERNED EFFECTS

Decorative patterned effects can be obtained using the appropriate equipment, in conjunction with pearlized dressings, shadow sprays or spirit dye solutions.

OTHER DRESSING METHODS

Other methods of dressing poromerics are available, such as wax creams or silicone creams. These are advantageous in that cleaning and dressing can be done in one operation, but they do not offer much lustre control.

With these methods, only a very thin film is applied and the surface of the poromeric is hardly affected. Wear properties will virtually be those of the untreated poromerics.

These dressings, especially silicones, may become more widely applicable, particularly if poromerics themselves are supplied in any desired lustre.

CONCLUSIONS

To summarize, poromerics are dressed to upgrade the appearance of shoes after their passage through the shoe factory. Similar techniques are used as with leather, although modified fillers and top dressings are required. To ensure good application of these fillers and top sprays thorough cleaning with a solvent-based cleaner is necessary.

CHAPTER 13

Impact of poromerics on shoe machinery

N. V. GERMANY

INTRODUCTION

ORIGINALLY, this paper was to have contained a moderate blend of technical and practical information, but as the previous authors have eroded the technical content of it away, I have decided to concentrate mainly on the practical aspects. Unfortunately, this too is not without some difficulty because I think I could complete it in two words— no problems. A slight over-simplification no doubt, but not too far from the truth.

Rather than present a mere discourse on the 'dos and don'ts' I will try to highlight the machinery operations where the special properties of poromerics could present some problems.

IMPACT OF POROMERICS

The word 'synthetic' was first treated with suspicion because of adverse reaction of the public, but later, especially when poromerics were introduced, it became synonymous with visions of new shoemaking methods and techniques.

Although poromerics have been successfully handled by conventional machinery, the financial breakeven point is still a long way off. The alternative of a material demanding a completely new shoe manufacturing plant would be a far too speculative venture.

Special note must be made of the following three poromeric properties because they affect many shoemaking operations:

1 They are susceptible to surface damage from pressure and heat
2 They are not as easy as leather to set, mould or fold because of their rubbery nature
3 They do not shrink or condense in the same way as leather.

Although these properties may create problems that seem formidable to overcome at first, if we ignore the differences between various types of poromerics, we then have within each type of material a very predictable article. Therefore, although each material has certain difficult characteristics, because they are predictable, shoe machinery can be set to do the job very satisfactorily.

Shoe manufacturers are likely to obtain their greatest savings when using poromerics if they turn their main attention to material stocking, planning, and cutting.

Undoubtedly a large travelling head type of cutting machine will ultimately be the machine for cutting poromerics, but for the time being this sort of machine might not be a practical proposition for some manufacturers; therefore, cutting must be done with existing equipment. Some attention to material handling might make cutting from the roll possible even with the swing beam type of press. The use of a material holder such as the No. 2 Cloth Holding Device in conjunction with a clicking press could be a useful interim solution (see Figs 13.1 and 13.2). No claim is made that this is equal in convenience to the Travelling Head Cutting Press, but it does avoid the need for installing a relatively costly machine before there is adequate use for such a machine in the factory.

Much has been written about the difference in resistance to stretch compared across the roll to along the roll (see Fig. 13.3), and advice as to which way to cut patterns is readily available. I do not wish to add to this other than to reiterate the need for patterns to allow for lasting with the minimum stress.

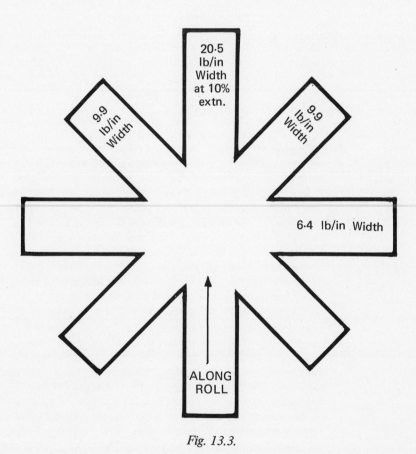

Fig. 13.3.

Always there is a danger in generalizing, but it is safe to say that very little trouble is being experienced with the majority of closing operations. Those operations needing some care are where heat and pressure are applied. Pressure damage is the main danger. Be sure and see that serrated pressure feet of sewing machines only apply just enough pressure to feed the work. The same goes for any machines feeding by serrated wheels. Overheating during any ironing on the back of tapes should be avoided. To show the effect of heat on these poromerics, Fig. 13.4(a) and (b) show graded heating from $140°C$ up to $240°C$. It will be seen that serious heat damage commences at about $180°C$ or just above. These samples were in contact with a hot surface for about 1 minute. Fig. 13.4(c) is a sample of pvc.

Skiving operations can be adequately performed on any current machinery. Any slight tendency for surface tackiness to create a drag during feeding can be overcome by applying ptfe tape to any of the stationary surfaces that the material comes in contact with during the operation. A flat shoulder scarf is usually recommended for folding operations and many existing skiving machines can be converted for this operation.

The thermo cementing and folding operation demands a very shallow scarf in order to avoid removing the whole of the base material. This is because the hot melt cement is not always a suitable cement for adhesion to the top layer, and it sometimes requires a base material to base material contact to obtain an adequate stick. The tendency for the material to reassert itself and open up before the cement can cool off is a problem.

However, the cement TC 9400 is usually quite adequate, but in certain cases where extra strength of bond is necessary, Be Be Rod 104 is an adequate alternative. There is a polyester type cement available for vinyl-based materials, but this is completely incompatible with the usual cement. This means that machines that have previously used TCF 9400 require a thorough clean before loading with TCF 500. The new cement has a higher melting point than TCF 9400, therefore the machine also needs a change of heating element in the crease foot holder.

With respect to the inability to condense these materials to the same degree as with leather, it is necessary to take extra care when negotiating an outside curve in the folding machine. Any tendency for the operator to try and beat the pleating feed rate of the machine round an outside curve will lead to bunching up of the material, resulting in poor pleating and a lack of consolidation of the fold.

Poromerics do not suit HF welding as well as pvc materials, but a great deal has been done by SATRA to investigate how to use this welding method. I would only mention that the overall appearance of the edge of materials, that have a substantial thickness of polyurethane for the top layer, rarely has the edge roundness that simulates a folded edge obtained from a pvc coating. This is because the flow properties at the temperatures used in the RF welding and cutting machine are poorer with polyurethane than pvc.

Forepart forming is one operation that would seem to be ideally suited to poromeric materials, but in actual fact their susceptibility to heat damage and the difficulty of heat setting has made the operation a critical one. Whilst many experiments have been carried out on forepart forming, the results so far indicate that the best help to lasting can be obtained from pattern cutting. However, some degree of blocking can be achieved by using a moderate amount of heat conditioning, and stretching the material in the newer variety of wide blade blocking machinery.

When backseaming, care should be taken to set the correct pressure in order to prevent marking of the face of the material. A woven backseam tape has been proved to be superior to that of the low tack adhesive paper tape. This is usually used in conjunction with a taping and seam pressing machine.

Linings and backers with low melt adhesive film for ironing-on are particularly suitable. It is recommended that the surface to which the face of the material is in contact should be clean and free from any foreign matter that may mark the material (see Fig. 13.5). Here again note that attention must be paid to temperature and surface marking.

So far, I have been referring to the less critical part of shoemaking with poromerics, but moving on to lasting brings me to the point of examining further what some of the properties of poromerics mean to these operations.

We now have to look at the stretch/break properties as well as those already mentioned. Taking tearing strength first, poromerics range from about equal to leather to about half the strength of leather, but here again it is dangerous to generalize. It is far better to compare one particular poromeric to the actual leather used for a particular application. However, in the main, poromerics are unlikely to have a greater tear strength than a reasonably good upper leather.

Tear strength on its own is not necessarily the only guide to lasting, but if related to break stretch, together they can be a yardstick to satisfactory lasting. We use the 'trouser' test for tear, and find the percentage of stretch to break to measure the break stretch. Having tested a large number of materials and knowing that they can be lasted satisfactorily, we have plotted tear strength against break stretch and obtained what we call a 180 rule, i.e. a curve that is represented by the product of tear strength and break stretch equalling 180.

Fig. 13.6 shows the curve with a number of test results plotted for various poromeric materials. Each line represents a different poromeric and AC is the result for across the roll, and AL is along. You will see the examples that are given are above the 180 curve, and as previously mentioned we know too that they last satisfactorily. However, if a result falls below that line into the shaded area we do not necessarily say that it will not last, but only that there is a danger of lasting strains causing tear or break.

The choice of toe puff material is important, especially in men s shoes. The selection of a very hard toe puff might exaggerate the sinking behind the toe puff which can be caused by poor heat setting, or over straining during lasting when less than ideal patterns are used (see Fig. 13.7). We have found that the Tufflex TR puff has the degree of softness that helps to avoid the hard line or sinking.

In ladies' shoes there is just the same danger but it is usually avoided by the ladies' toe puffs being more resilient than men's in any case. Solvent-type puffs should be avoided. If residual solvent is retained by

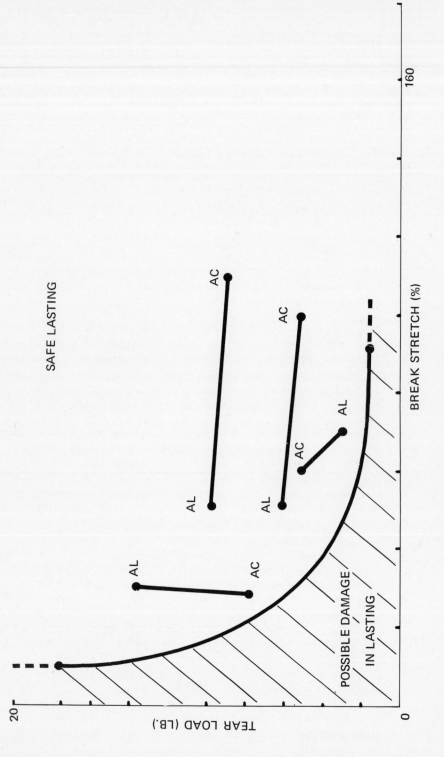

Fig. 13.6.

Fig. 13.7.

the puff when the lasting strains are applied, there is a danger of penetration through to the top surface of the upper material, resulting in damage.

In the case of the seat, thermoplastic counters are quite satisfactory as long as the heating and pressure during conditioning prior to the backpart moulding operation are not too severe. The mould bands should have a smooth surface so that there is no damage caused to the top coat of the upper material.

In the lasting machines themselves, given good patterns, no trouble will be experienced as long as we avoid the dangers described earlier in this this paper, i.e. to avoid overheating, abrasion, and heavy pressures. Fig. 13.8 shows wiper plate damage. Wiper plates must be cool, possibly cool enough to handle and the lasting margin wants to be just adequate for the job. If the lasting margins are too wide there is a bunching of material, and if cement lasting, the bunching of material will cause a breakaway from the insole giving a poor bond. The large pleats will require heavy scouring to produce a flat toe and there is always the danger that material will be removed over the featherline. Throughout lasting it must be remembered that the flame-type of wrinkle chasing is not to be advised, and therefore, the lasting job has got to create the correct featherline of the shoe rather than repairing operations afterwards.

Making and finishing are fairly straightforward so long as the previously mentioned rules are observed. Care must be taken over upper roughing, but people who have used these materials have not found the operation as serious a problem as was originally expected. A lightweight wire brush has been found to be satisfactory for roughing these materials as long as the roughing is kept within the featherline and the top coat is removed.

In the case of materials with a woven interlayer some experimenting has shown that a grit-type wheel avoids fluffing. However, many thousands of poromeric shoes have been roughed satisfactorily with a wire brush and this must indicate that there is a greater degree of tolerance than might have been believed at first.

Fig. 13.9 shows a shoe that was roughed on the B.U. Automatic Upper Roughing Machine. The brushes used in the automatic machine were a

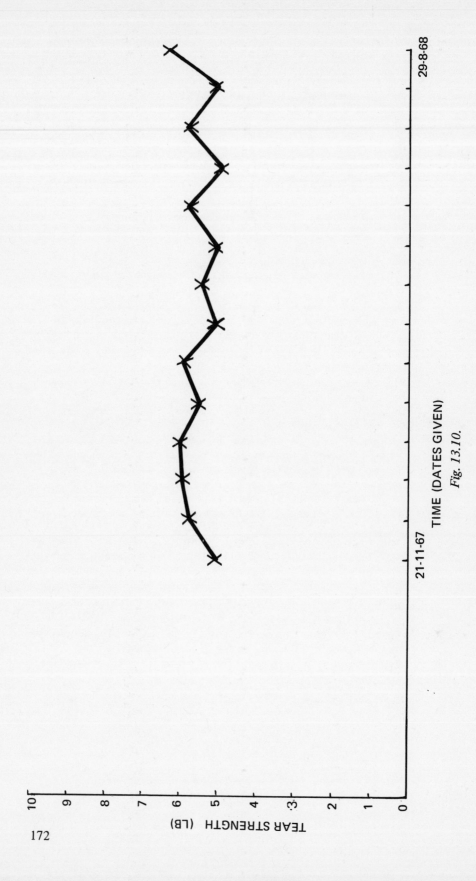

TIME (DATES GIVEN)
Fig. 13.10.

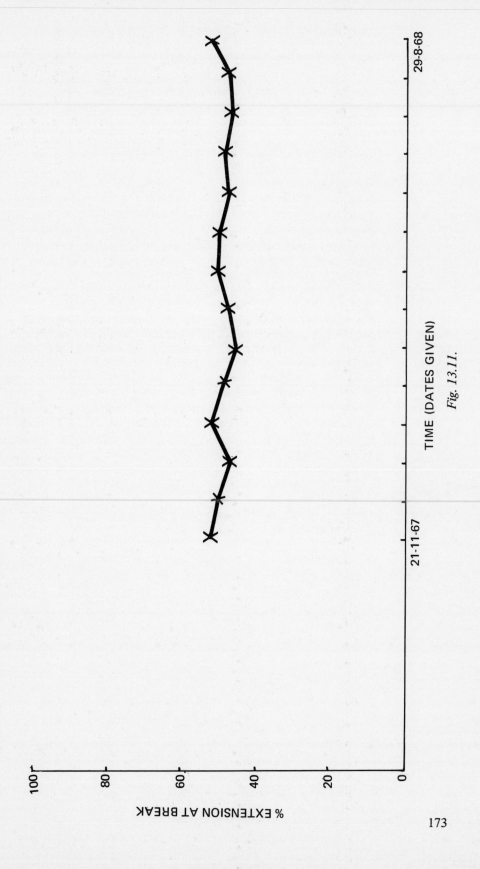

Fig. 13.11.

more flexible type made from a smaller diameter wire than used on leather.

If normal care is taken to avoid frictional heat from cutter shields, then no trouble will be experienced during edge trimming. The way of overcoming this frictional heat is to have a free-running cutter shield. It will be seen from the comments in this paper that the problems of handling these materials are not too great. In future the consistency of the properties of the materials is going to be appreciated to a greater extent, and shoe manufacturers themselves will gain confidence from having materials with such predictable characteristics. Examples of this consistency are given in Figs 13.10 and 13.11, which show how little variation there was in the tear strength and extension at break of a particular poromeric over a nine months' check period.

Many prophesies have been made about the future of poromerics in connection with machinery development, but I think that shoe manufacturers are more likely to be the first to exploit their main properties, i.e. uniformity and consistency, rather than machinery designers. However, this will not materialize until manufacturers have long runs of poromerics without there being an interdispersion of shoes made in other materials. Almost without exception we can see that present machinery will handle these materials, but what is important is that care must be taken to set the machinery to avoid the pitfalls that, in the past with leather, have not been evident. It is a pity to complete a good looking shoe, well made, bottomed and finished and find that due to careless handling it has marks which cannot be repaired.

Finally, one must understand the main characteristics of poromerics: this means beware of too much heat and pressure and do not overpull in lasting, and then good shoes can be produced. Probably my opening two words should be altered to 'almost no problems'.

ACKNOWLEDGEMENTS

I wish to acknowledge the help of Mr K. Lee and Mr R. Upton of B.U.S.M. Co Ltd, in producing this paper.

CHAPTER 14

Poromeric footwear marketing and customer reaction

W. N. HOOD

REDEMPTION OF DEVELOPMENT COSTS—PRICING POLICY

THE marketing of poromerics, both as a material and made up as footwear, is the reward of all previous research and development and must be profitable if the material is to succeed.

The cost of research and development of poromeric material will directly affect the marketing strategy of the poromeric manufacturer and the shoe manufacturer. The actual cost of manufacturing the poromeric will initially bear little relationship to the price charged to the shoe manufacturer, unless the poromeric manufacturer risks losing profit at the start of the life cycle of his product in the hope that the product qualities combined with low prices are sufficient to get market saturation and high volume to give him the profit redemption necessary to clear his research and development costs and to exclude competitors.

The speed of redemption is determined by actual manufacturing costs and actual R & D costs allied to the product properties and competitive behaviour. The result of this mix determines the cost of the product to the shoe manufacturer.

As poromerics and poromeric footwear in the UK are an innovation, they require a pioneer pricing policy. The critical task in this pricing policy is the correct prediction of sales behaviour, and in the initial pricing of a poromeric there are two choices:

1 A policy of high initial pricing that skims the cream of demand through using the poromeric in high-class footwear.
2 A policy of low price from the outset striving for quick and wide market penetration.

The actual range is wider than this but this division clarifies the issues.

The direct advantage of the high price policy is the speedy redemption of R & D costs.

Thorough studies by behavioural scientists of the consumer motivation to purchase and particularly the adoption process of a new product clearly show that the market segment for a new product is narrow. Poromeric footwear must be marketed to this particular segment. A high price article has an automatic status feel that works to the product's advantage and encourages sales amongst the pacesetters and the early adopters of the public.

Starting with a high price shoe the poromeric manufacturer is attacking a market segment that is relatively unsusceptible to price pressures and

175

is the least value-conscious segment. Subsequent price reductions with attendant good public relations to the consumer and to the shoe trade will still allow a profit to be made and expose the product to a far larger market. This downward trend in pricing by poromeric manufacturers is already evident.

Disadvantages of the high price policy are clear:

The high price policy prevents quick sales to the many buyers at the lower end of the income scale both in terms of consumer and manufacturer.

It prevents large sales which could produce higher R & D redemption totals more quickly. This involves the delicate formula for maximizing volume and profit.

The high price policy prevents the exclusion of competitors at low prices and a high price policy may stimulate other manufacturers to pursue a low price wide penetration policy.

The pricing policy both of the poromeric manufacturer and of the shoe manufacturer using poromerics is part of the marketing mix and must be considered closely in conjunction with the product properties.

ADVERTISING PROMOTION AND LIFE CYCLE

Each footwear manufacturer has a different approach to advertising, but all manufacturers use advertising in some form. This may range from the decoration of a seat sock to a large national press and TV advertising campaign. But whatever the form of advertising the intentions of the advertising as applied to poromeric footwear are the same for every company large or small. Fundamentally the intention is that the advertising should finally cause profit to be made through sales to consumers of poromeric footwear.

The speed of reaction of consumers to advertising is critical. We know that in 1967, whilst consumers were aware that uppers were made from materials other than leather, only 2% knew of the existence of any poromeric by name. Even now consumer knowledge of poromerics is very small.

American and English research confirms the experience of synthetic fibre manufacturers that consumers have an inherent resistance to change and particularly an inherent resistance to change from natural (leather) to synthetic (poromeric). It is the reduction of this resistance that is the biggest task for advertising poromerics at the present stage in the product life cycle.

No manufacturer of poromerics has or will have a monopoly of the sales of poromeric upper materials. Manufacturers of poromerics and shoe manufacturers using poromerics must accept that any advertising of a specific poromeric will encourage consumer acceptance of the idea of the use of poromerics in footwear, and contribute to a reduction in the resistance to change from natural to synthetic.

The consumer will compare any statement of product benefits about poromeric footwear with the established performance of tried footwear; this will mean a comparison with leather.

The acceptance of poromerics, particularly by men, will be accelerated by the existing acceptance of synthetic fibres in clothing. The introduction of poromerics in footwear is not the pioneer of the synthetic introduction list, and consumer reaction to poromeric advertising will be comparatively speedy. This speed works to the advantage of the innovators in the poromeric field. Those manufacturers who are in effective mass production have an advantage over the manufacturers who are only at the research or pilot manufacture stage.

Existing manufacturers may be able to saturate the market for poromeric footwear in terms of consumer awareness, product distribution, and price range penetration. But the price of existing widely used poromerics has meant their introduction in the upper/middle price brackets and this leaves room for manoeuvre in the lower/middle price brackets with the attendant high volume sales potential. Maybe existing manufacturers will redeem their development costs quickly and enter these high volume sales fields themselves as soon as effective competition appears.

The shoe trade, which is regarded as a somewhat traditional industry, appears to have no inhibitions about adopting something comparatively revolutionary in product terms. The industry is already conditioned by the success of synthetic soles and heels, and the consumer acceptance of synthetic linings. Any change in shoe product materials is influenced a great deal by the behaviour of the large distributive organizations and the large shoe manufacturers who have not been slow in using poromeric materials. These large companies are in their turn affected and attracted by the considerable marketing resources of the manufacturers of poromeric materials, who without exception are divisions of vast companies.

This trading atmosphere both amongst consumers and amongst the shoe trade means a quick reaction to the advertising of poromerics.

Advertising is expensive and is purposely avoided by many shoe manufacturers whose metier is to produce products to sell on the basis of a cheap price and/or high margin to the distributor. Such a shoe manufacturer who uses poromerics can be assisted in his sales by the advertising of the poromeric manufacturer. What is important is the shoe manufacturer who wishes to distinguish his shoes made from a branded poromeric rather than be content with demand for his shoes because they are made from a well-known and advertised branded poromeric.

A complication to this already involved mix between a specific brand of shoe and a specific brand of poromeric is the growth of private labelling of shoes by the largest shoe multiples and distributors. An outstanding·feature of consumer shoe purchasing behaviour is the large amount of window shopping just before a purchase is made. This window shopping works in favour of the shoe distributor who captures the consumer's interest at point of purchase by displaying the private label brand of shoe using an already nationally advertised poromeric.

Consumer advertising of poromeric materials and shoes made from poromeric materials is introductory in its nature at present. Sophistications of advertising to introduce additional uses for a poromeric or to highlight distinguishing benefits of each poromeric will follow as the life cycle of poromerics progresses and as the competition and number of competitors changes. Knowledge of the product life cycle of any poromeric material and of shoes made using that poromeric material is essential in effective manipulation of marketing and consumer reaction to poromeric footwear.

We are more aware than most industries of the cyclical nature of consumer behaviour. We are supposed to suffer from a four-year consumer purchasing cycle, and we encourage an annual cycle by the introduction of fashion in shoes.

In the life cycle of shoes using poromeric material we are in the market development stage in the UK.

There is little demand from the consumer, there is almost no repeat purchase, and in consumer terms the product is not widely known or accepted. Sales are low, and, in relation to total shoes sold, the number of shoes sold using poromeric materials is insignificant.

At this stage of the life cycle a disproportionately large amount of finance is employed on communication/advertising, and is applied at this stage primarily by the poromeric material manufacturers.

Existing manufacturers of poromerics are in a hurry to capitalize on the singular position that they will only enjoy for a short time in the product life cycle. They are only one of a few innovators at the present time and in every case they have colossal resources behind them that can be used to promote and advertise their product. They will not advertise their product until they are certain that the product is technically correct.

The life cycle does not start with the introduction to the consumer of the product; it starts with the investment in research and development. This investment must be redeemed as early as possible in the life cycle and yet this coincides with a time of high advertising and marketing costs.

The next stage in the life cycle of poromerics will be a period of market growth which is the 'take-off' stage. When the sales curve for a new range of poromeric shoes begins to take off, it is at this time more than any other that competitive manufacturers will be attracted to the market and some manufacturers may capitalize and improve on the innovator's marketing effort. At this stage the shoe manufacturers' advertising effort will shift from persuasion to try the product to persuasion to prefer the company brand, and changes in advertising and marketing emphasis are necessary.

Looking further ahead along the life cycle to maturity of sales and decline of sales of poromeric footwear the uncertainty of forecasting grows. But a thoughtful guess is better than ignoring any forecast at all.

The extent of the success of poromerics in footwear is difficult to evaluate. Du Pont's estimate of 15% of the total shoe market within five years is probably as good as any.

One essential feature of poromeric advertising so far in the UK has been the effort applied to encourage distribution of poromeric footwear amongst shoe retailers. Analysis is nebulous, but spot checks in trade journals show an unusually large proportion of advertising appropriation is channelled into trade propaganda. It is expensive for the shoe manufacturer to advertise to the consumer without having adequate retail distribution; to a certain extent such expense is inevitable as the shoe buyers show caution at the time of introduction of a poromeric. They will not buy large quantities of any poromeric footwear until they are reassured of consumer acceptance and such reassurance can only be established at this stage if supported by an amount of consumer advertising which results in encouraging consumer call off from the shops.

CUSTOMER REACTION

At present poromeric materials used in footwear are sold to the consumer either declared or undeclared by advertising and promotion. It is incorrect to infer that declared poromerics have product advantages over leather that are worth promoting, and that undeclared poromerics are inferior to leather but probably cheaper than leather.

The undeclared poromeric does not have the expensive burden of advertising and promotion costs included in the price of the shoes and shoes marketed under this method are often in the lower price categories. As already stated the pricing policy of poromerics is indivisible from the product properties.

Poromerics impress three properties upon consumers:

1 A favourable comparison with leather—the word 'Breathing' as a reassurance is almost invariably included in spoken or written advertising copy
2 The appearance is smarter and maintenance is easier than with other established types of footwear
3 The initial good looks do not deteriorate as quickly as any other established types of footwear.

World-wide it is becoming clear that men's footwear is most suited to the properties of poromerics. There are few men's shoes made using non-poromeric synthetic upper materials as the upper pattern of men's shoes encloses the foot more completely than does the women's shoe pattern. Women's shoes require less breathing/poromeric qualities and the use of pvc materials, for instance, has less effect on footwear comfort compared with the use of poromerics in women's shoes, and in most cases pvc is cheaper.

However precisely we may define poromerics, the Marketing Manager must realize that to the consumer, poromeric = synthetic = some degree of resistance to purchase.

It follows that any declared poromeric must have properties that can overcome the inherent consumer bias against synthetics. The statement of a poromeric brand name is insufficient, there must be an attendant demonstration of consumer benefit resulting from the use of the branded poromeric. Once the brand name and brand properties are established then the statement of the brand name only may be sufficient, but at the present time in the life cycle of poromerics used in footwear a demonstration of brand properties is essential.

The introduction of synthetics is readily accepted in non-personal consumer durables or semi-durables, such as motor car tyres and kitchen utensils. With clothing and shoes the adoption is less sure. When nylon shirts were first introduced some consumers who purchased nylon shirts were enthusiastic about the product and experienced no discomfort, others were less enthusiastic and uncomfortable when wearing the shirt. It seems there will be similar experiences with poromeric footwear. There are some people whose feet are just not suited to poromeric materials regardless of whether there is leather lining or synthetic lining or whether the soles are leather or synthetic.

A thorough wear trial of poromeric footwear in the winter of 1967/68 in the UK using a sample of 450 trialists included a question in a monthly survey— 'Do you notice any unusual foot temperature when wearing your trial shoes—if yes, hot or cold?' Eighty trialists answered yes, and of these 32 reported colder foot temperature and 48 reported hotter foot temperature. Of the 450 trialists only half knew that the shoes had uppers of poromeric material and of the 80 trialists who mentioned a change in foot temperature 60 were aware that the shoes were not made with leather uppers.

Experience in North America of consumer reaction to poromerics is valuable in forecasting product acceptance in the UK. In North America about 18% of all men's shoes sold have poromeric uppers. What is more important is that repeat purchases contribute a normal fraction of this 18% figure. The macro-economic background in the UK is similar to America and there is no reason why there will not be a similar degree of consumer acceptance of poromerics in the UK shoe market.

Shoes are judged by consumers as good or bad by the amount of trouble that they do or do not cause. Trouble is judged in terms of comfort and need of care. The latter quality, the convenience factor, is most important as has been proved by the success of Hush Puppies. The two sources of trouble, comfort and care, are deliberately studied closely by consumers at point of shoe purchase. This unusual amount of deliberate study, which is peculiar to purchases of shoes and clothing, works in favour of poromerics provided correct and generous fitting is evident when the shoe is first worn in the shoe shop. Promoted features, particularly ease of cleaning, and retention of good looks, will increase the ultimate success of poromeric footwear.

Good fitting of shoes with poromeric uppers is essential; we know that incorrect fitting can generate five times as much perspiration from the foot if the shoes are tight. This extraordinary perspiration causes discomfort and removes any chance of user recommendation. It is user recommendation which is the most effective and dynamic instrument that can ensure the failure or success of poromeric footwear.

INDEX